A Framework for Government Research and Development

Presented to Parliament by
The Lord Privy Seal
by Command of Her Majesty
November 1971

LONDON
HER MAJESTY'S STATIONERY OFFICE
Reprinted 1973
52½p net

Cmnd. 4814

SBN 10 148140 3

CONTENTS

A FRAMEWORK FOR GOVERNMENT RESEARCH
AND DEVELOPMENT

1. In the White Paper on the Reorganisation of Central Government (Cmnd. 4506) it was announced that all Ministers were reviewing the functions of their departments, placing emphasis on ensuring that wherever possible, at all levels, responsibility and accountability were clearly defined and allocated. The need was also indicated for a clear and comprehensive definition of Government strategy which could be systematically developed to take account of changing circumstances and could provide a framework within which the Government's policies as a whole could be more effectively formulated.

2. These studies of course include departmental activities in the field of research and development and as part of this process the Government commissioned a report from Lord Rothschild, the Head of the Central Policy Review Staff, on Government research and development. In addition, they sought advice, through the Council for Scientific Policy, on the most effective arrangements for organising and supporting pure and applied scientific research and post-graduate training.

3. The Government have now received reports from both Lord Rothschild and the Council for Scientific Policy, and have decided to publish both of them in full as a basis for consultation on the future organisation of Government research and development. They are included as appendices to this Green Paper.

4. The Government welcome the recommendation in the report by Lord Rothschild that applied research and development commissioned by the Government should be controlled in accordance with a ' customer/contractor ' principle which is already being applied in certain areas. The report also considers the implications of adopting this principle for the Science Budget of the Department of Education and Science and the work of the Research Councils. The Government note that the report of the Council for Scientific Policy is not at variance with this principle.

5. The Government endorse the ' customer/contractor ' principle and consider that it should be implemented in respect of applied research and development carried out or sponsored by the Government, whether by the Research Councils or elsewhere. The Government believe that, subject to this principle, it would be right to preserve the Research Councils under the sponsorship of the Department of Education and Science. It is also the Government's view that it would continue to be desirable for a body of authoritative advice to be available to the Secretary of State for Education and Science on the allocation of her Department's Science Budget.

6. Before reaching decisions on the detailed application of the ' customer/contractor ' principle, the Government intend to allow time for wide public debate and to discuss the issues involved with the scientific community. Discussions will therefore be held with the Royal Societies, the Council for

Scientific Policy, the Research Councils and the appropriate Staff Associations. The Government will aim to complete these discussions by 29 February 1972 and to publish their final conclusions in a White Paper as soon as possible thereafter.

7. Written comments from other interested parties would be welcomed by the Government. These should be addressed to the Government's Chief Scientific Adviser at the Cabinet Office, Whitehall, London S.W.1, and should be received not later than Friday 14 January 1972.

THE ORGANISATION AND MANAGEMENT OF GOVERNMENT R. & D.

By

LORD ROTHSCHILD
HEAD OF THE CENTRAL POLICY REVIEW STAFF

THE ORGANISATION AND MANAGEMENT OF GOVERNMENT R. & D.

BY LORD ROTHSCHILD, HEAD OF THE CENTRAL POLICY REVIEW STAFF

Contents

THE ORGANISATION AND MANAGEMENT OF GOVERNMENT R. & D.

BY LORD ROTHSCHILD, HEAD OF THE CENTRAL POLICY REVIEW STAFF

CHAPTER I

INTRODUCTION

1. One might expect that a review of Government research and development (R. & D.) would be greatly concerned with answers to such questions as:

(a) Are we doing too much, too little, or about the right amount of R. & D.?

(b) Is the balance between pure and applied research about right?

(c) Should we do more intramural and less extramural R. & D., or *vice versa*?

(d) What R. & D. are we doing which should not be done?

(e) What R. & D. should we do which is not being done?

(f) Is there adequate machinery, at the centre, critically to evaluate the overall R. & D. scene?

2. These questions, and possible answers to them, are not systematically discussed in this report because to try and do so would not help to provide a framework in which the efficiency of Government R. & D. can be maximised. The questions either relate to an out-of-date concept of R. & D. management, or they are unanswerable. The resolution of the dilemma, which is more apparent than real, is to ensure that the organisation and management of R. & D. is logical, flexible, humane and decentralised, the prerequisites of an efficient system. Furthermore, that each person in the system has clearly defined responsibilities. This report is, therefore, concerned with the establishment of the principles on which such an efficient system must rest and the consequences of accepting and implementing them.

3. Some comments may, however, be made about the six questions enumerated above. (a) is discussed later; (b) is not a meaningful question because there cannot be a correct ' balance ' between the resources devoted to pure and applied research. The amount of pure research done at Universities and elsewhere depends on the talent and money available; but one can make certain assertions about the proportion of pure research permissible or necessary within an applied research programme. Questions (c), (d) and (e) are automatically answered when a satisfactory organisation for the management and prosecution of R. & D. exists and it is one of the purposes of this report to recommend one. Question (f) is difficult to answer, because it is doubtful whether any central body can or should try critically to evaluate the Government's R. & D. as a whole. Nevertheless, some focal point, i.e. the Chief Scientific Adviser, is necessary at the centre, not only to satisfy the general desire for such focal points, but also to co-ordinate trans-departmental and trans-national subjects involving R. & D. The phrase ' subjects involving R. & D.' is deliberate and intended to emphasise that applied R. & D., with

which this report is mainly concerned, is not an activity in its own right; it is part of a wider process, for reasons that are discussed at length in the following pages.

TOO MUCH R. & D., TOO LITTLE, OR JUST ABOUT RIGHT?

4. In spite of many books and papers, some of a mathematical nature, no-one, in industry or Government, has found a method of determining the ' right ' amount of R. & D. to do. In fact, most research directors and R. & D. administrators admit that decisions on this matter are an art rather than a science. Nevertheless, the person who has to pay for the end-product of applied R. & D. is, for obvious reasons, in the best position to decide how much he can afford. Depending on his qualifications, he may need to take the advice of scientists, mathematicians or engineers skilled in the subject under consideration.

5. Some people believe that eminent scientists, mathematicians and engineers should have an opportunity to express an overall view on the nation's R. & D. to those ultimately in charge. But such an overall view, whether greatly desired or even ordered, is of questionable value. Some comfort—or discomfort—may, for example, be gained from comparisons with other countries, see Table 1.

TABLE 1

PUBLIC EXPENDITURE ON RESEARCH AND DEVELOPMENT IN
VARIOUS COUNTRIES

(1970 figures except where stated)

	Total (£m.)	Civil (£m.)
United States (1969)	6,652	3,393
Germany	725	600
France	735	510
United Kingdom	581	353
Japan (1969)	351	344
Italy...	191	185
Netherlands	128	122
Belgium	52	50

The countries in this Table almost certainly define R. & D. in different ways; they have widely different populations; and they are at different stages of industrial development. The reader may, therefore, feel that the figures should be divided by some factor or factors to take account of these differences; but the question is, by what? If this exercise is not undertaken, if only because it is unclear how to do it, the reader may derive some satisfaction from the United Kingdom being ' about in the middle '. Why, on the other hand, does France spend more than us? Should this be a matter for satisfaction or discomfort? Leaving aside this difficult or, perhaps, unanswerable question, one must remember that the R. & D. effort of a country will have no effect on that country's welfare for at least seven years after the date of the effort in question; so that no inferences can be made from the figures in Table 1 until, at the earliest, 1977. Even then the inferences will be of questionable value because it is not, for example, known whether an increase in G.N.P. is in part caused by an increase in R. & D. expenditure, or whether the latter is a consequence of increased prosperity. Writers sometimes seem confused about this point.

CHAPTER II

APPLIED R. & D.

PRINCIPLES

6. This report is based on the principle that applied R. & D., that is R. & D. with a practical application as its objective, must be done on a customer-contractor basis. The customer says what he wants; the contractor *R. 1*(¹) does it (if he can); and the customer pays. Basic, fundamental or pure research, called basic research in this report, has no analogous customer-contractor basis(²), though those engaged in such work may and, sometimes, too often do become involved in applied R. & D. The words customer and contractor are discussed in detail later. Here, some observations about basic and applied R. & D. are necessary. Much time can be lost in semantic arguments about the nature of basic research, its impact, accidental or otherwise, on applied research, and the difference between them; and the same applies to research and development. It is sometimes said, for example, that development should be done by different people, in a different place, and with a different administrative system from research. The reverse is the case, whenever possible. It is also sometimes said, in justification of basic research, that chance observations made during such work, and their subsequent study, may be just as important as those made during applied R. & D. While there is some truth in this contention, the country's needs are not so trivial as to be left to the mercies of a form of scientific roulette, with many more than the conventional 37 numbers on which the ball may land.

7. The end-product or objective of applied R. & D. is:

(a) *A Product*, e.g. a tank, an antibiotic, a nuclear reactor, an artificial hand, an instrument for measuring the concentration of nitrogen oxides in exhaust gases, or a drought-resistant variety of wheat;

(b) *A Process*, e.g. for the manufacture of an antibiotic, for converting natural gas into protein, for purifying uranium from uranium oxide, or for removing nitrogen oxides from exhaust gases;

(c) *A Method of Operation*, e.g. to prevent collisions in the English Channel, to speed up the delivery of letters, or to give advice, sometimes in the discharge of a statutory obligation.

(¹) *R* stands for recommendation.
(²) It is scarcely meaningful or productive to stretch the customer-contractor principle to the extent of claiming that the Department of Education and Science (D.E.S.) is a customer who says ' I want good science, basic research and education, and am prepared to pay for it '.

The end-product of basic research is an increase in knowledge. In more sophisticated language, basic research is concerned with the discovery of rational correlations and principles.

8. The Government supports basic research and commissions applied R. & D. The former is almost exclusively financed by the Department of Education and Science (D.E.S.) and the latter by all the other Departments which commission R. & D. The D.E.S. supports basic research, *via* the University Grants Committee, at the Universities; and *via* the Council for Scientific Policy (C.S.P.) and ' subordinate ' Research Councils, at the Research Councils' own institutes, units and elsewhere. The five Research Councils are only ' subordinate ' to the C.S.P. in respect of the allocation of funds. They are autonomous in respect of their programmes, an unsatisfactory situation in some cases, which is the subject of recommendations in this report. According to the D.E.S. an appreciable part of the work of the Medical Research Council (M.R.C.); and a major part of the work of the Agricultural Research Council (A.R.C.) and of the Natural Environment Research Council (N.E.R.C.) is ' applied '. But this work had and has no customer to commission and approve it. This is wrong. However distinguished, intelligent and practical scientists may be, they cannot be so well qualified to decide what the needs of the nation are, and their priorities, as those responsible for ensuring that those needs are met. This is why applied R. & D. must have a
R. 2 customer, whose role is described immediately below.

THE CUSTOMER

9. The customer (client, user, or their representative) may be direct, for example the Vice-Chief of the Naval Staff who requires a new or improved torpedo; or indirect, in that he represents, sometimes in quite an oblique way, the user of the product, process, or method of operation which constitutes the end-product of an applied R. & D. programme. An example is road R. & D., sponsored by the Department of the Environment (D.O.E.) on behalf of the motorist (at any rate in part). The customer should have the following responsibilities or accountabilities[1]:

R. 3   (a) He should decide, with advice or on his own initiative, that an R. & D. programme is needed to achieve a specific objective.

Note

Unspecific or unduly general objectives such as ' We must find out all about the physiology of domestic farm animals ' or ' We must be able to describe engine knock in precise physico-chemical terms ' should be treated with caution, however admirable they may seem at first glance. More often than not they imply financial and scientific commitments of an open-ended nature. These are rarely justifiable in an applied R. & D. programme.

R. 4   (b) He should decide how much can be spent on the programme. (Reference is made to operating expenditure, not capital expenditure on equipment.)

---

[1] The word accountability is used in its normal sense. i.e. someone who is accountable is not necessarily an Accounting Officer.

Notes

(i) The customer will normally need the advice of the Chief Scientist (q.v.) and the Controller R. & D. (q.v.), the latter being, *inter alia*, a specialist on programme costs and the relationship between them and estimated completion dates.

(ii) The word ' spent ' does not imply the physical transfer of funds. It *R. 5* is, however, recommended that the amounts spent on different programmes should be formally debited, with account numbers, to the named, accountable customer.

(iii) Operating expenditure should include a depreciation or obsolescence *R. 6* charge.

(c) He should approve capital expenditure for the development, as op- *R. 7* posed to the research, phase of the programme, and for new research buildings.

Note.

Difficulties are sometimes raised about making a clear-cut distinction between research and development, and the familiar ' continuous R. & D. spectrum ' argument is adduced in support of these alleged difficulties. There are two ways of dealing with this question, whether the problem is a real one or not; first, by recognising that a development programme almost invariably costs at least ten times as much as the research component of the same programme; secondly, by accepting that development should very rarely be started until and unless there is a better than 90 per cent chance that the objective of the R. & D. programme will be realised.

(d) He should determine priorities between programmes. *R. 8*

THE CHIEF SCIENTIST

10. The Chief Scientist is part of the customer organisation for all departmental R. & D. This title is preferred to that of Chief Scientific Adviser because he must be closely associated with the customer in the decisions enumerated in paragraphs 9(a)–(d). Depending on the expertise within the ' divisions ' of which a Department is composed, and their R. & D. needs, the Chief Scientist may have representatives within them. This implies that a member of the Chief Scientists' organisation may have two bosses, the head of the division and the Chief Scientist. There is nothing organisationally abnormal or unsound about such a system; indeed, there are precedents for it within goverment at the present time. A similar situation arises when customers commission R. & D. at multifunctional laboratories (q.v.).

11. There should be no line relationship between the Chief Scientist and *R. 9* the Controller R. & D. (whose role is described immediately below). They are engaged in quite different activities.

R. 10 12. The Controller R. & D. should be the chief executive of the R. & D. function, the contractor providing an R. & D. service for the customer. He is the head office focal point to which the R. & D. function is accountable and, as such, is immune to parochial considerations which sometimes affect the Directors of individual research establishments, however objective they may aim to be. The R. & D. function consists of the research workers and their supporting staff, their laboratories or analogous institutions where they work, and a very small head office organisation in which the Controller R. & D. is located. The reason why there is only a skeleton head office organisation is *R. 11* because the Controller R. & D. should draw on his laboratories, often by secondment, for expertise. A scientist soon loses his skills if he does not use them.

R. 12 13. The Controller R. & D., like the customer, may commission work at Universities or other extramural organisations when his ' in-house ' organisation has not got the facilities or expertise needed to implement the customer's requirements.

R. 13 14. The Controller R. & D. should have the following responsibilities or accountabilities:

(*a*) to provide his customers with an efficient R. & D. service.

Notes

(i) ' An efficient R. & D. service ' covers a multitude of factors which will be well known to research administrators. They range from authorisation, within certain budgetary and administrative restraints, of capital expenditure on research but not on development equipment nor research buildings, to ensuring a proper flow of people into and out of the R. & D. function. The accountability of the Controller R. & D. for capital expenditure on research equipment involves two *R. 14* departures from current practice: first, operating and capital expenditure should not be lumped together as one cost item. Apart from other considerations, this avoids footnotes explaining ' exceptional items " such as the purchase, in a particular year, of a survey vessel. Secondly, accountability for operating and capital expendi- *R. 15* ture should not be vested in the same individual except, naturally, at the Permanent Secretary level. Expenditure at the development stage of a project, which is at least ten times as great as at the re- search stage—and has quite different probability criteria—naturally needs the customer's approval. It is, therefore, not the responsibility of the Controller R. & D. on his own.

(ii) The Controller R. & D. faces serious difficulties in ensuring a proper flux of people through the R. & D. function. This question is of sufficient importance to merit special discussion, see Chapter IV.

(*b*) to spend the 10 per cent General Research Surcharge .

Note—this subject is discussed immediately below.

15. Virtually all applied R. & D. laboratories, except those exclusively concerned with testing or technical service, sooner or later engage, overtly or clandestinely, in research which is not directly concerned with the programmes commissioned by the customers: and it is a good thing that they do. It is, however, important that such activities should be recognised as being necessary R. 16 and that they should be formally quantified. The average operating expendi- R. 17 ture on them should not amount to more than about 10 per cent of that sanctioned by the customers and the expenditure, which is a surcharge on the customers, should be wholly at the discretion of the Controller R. & D. R. 18 These activities are called General Research because they do not necessarily consist of applied R. & D., or of basic research. General Research is done for the following reasons:

    (a) to engage in basic research in a field relevant to the applied tasks of the laboratory, but which is not being done elsewhere, e.g. at a University;

    (b) to test out new, way-out and unprogrammed ideas of the scientists, engineers and mathematicians themselves;

    (c) to maintain expertise, e.g. to recruit and keep a spectroscopist who will not join the laboratory unless he can spend part of his time on his own research;

    (d) to facilitate the transition from academic life to that in an applied R. & D. organisation.

16. It is important to appreciate that the General Research surcharge of about 10 per cent is an *average* figure per Department. Some establishments may be almost wholly engaged in General Research, for example in molecular biology or superconductivity. Others may do very little—but the average expenditure must not be more than about 10 per cent of the departmental R. & D. budget and it is the Controller R. & D's. responsibility to see that it is not. There is no reason why the General Research surcharge should increase R. 19 a Department's overall R. & D. expenditure.

17. If the General Research surcharge principle were accepted now and if, for the time being, the D.E.S. payments were excluded, some £54 million would be spent on work in this category in 1971.

18. The D.E.S. is excluded 'for the time being' because until and unless the recommendations in this report are accepted, the D.E.S. Research Councils, to whom the D.E.S. will pay £109·5 million in 1971–72, do not conform with the customer-contractor concept. Apart from this, two of these Research Councils, concerned with 'Science' (£50·9 million) and 'Social Science' (£2·2 million) are not suitable for inclusion within this concept. Table 2 shows how the figure £54 million is arrived at, as 10 per cent of (£645·5 million − £109·5 million) = £53·6 million.

7

TABLE 2

DEPARTMENTAL R. & D. EXPENDITURE, 1971–72

	£ million
Ministry of Agriculture, Fisheries & Food	6·2
Department of Agriculture and Fisheries for Scotland	6·5
Ministry of Defence	259·3
Department of Education & Science (see also Table 3)	109·5
Department of the Environment*	33·2
Overseas Development Administration	3·5
Department of Health & Social Security ⎫	
Scottish Home & Health Department ⎬(Health)	10.9
Welsh Office ... ... ⎭	
Home Office	2·5
Department of Trade & Industry	205·0
Miscellaneous	8·9
	———
	645·5

* Including expenditure on R. & D. laboratories and accommodation for other Departments.

NEED FOR UNIFORM TERMINOLOGY

19. Departments which commission or ought to commission a significant amount of R. & D. should have within their headquarters a Chief Scientist and a Controller R. & D;. and, to avoid confusion between these two quite different jobs, the Chief Scientist-Controller R. & D. terminology should be
R. 20 adopted by all Departments except for the D.E.S. and, for the time being, the Home Office. The Department of Trade and Industry (D.T.I.) and the Department of the Environment (D.O.E.) will need time to become adjusted to this proposal. The recommendation that Departments should adopt this uniform terminology is not caused by a passion for tidiness; nor by any wish to indulge in semantic hair-splitting. At present, June 1971, the D.T.I., for example, has a Chief Scientist, some of whose duties are identical with those of a Controller R. & D., and a Chief Scientific Adviser (Energy). The Home Office has one man called 'Director General of Research and Chief Scientist'. The Ministry of Agriculture, Fisheries and Food (M.A.F.F.) has a Director General Agricultural Development and Advisory Services, who is partly concerned with R. & D., and a Chief Scientific Adviser (Food). The D.O.E. has a Director General of Research who has both Chief Scientist and Controller R. & D. responsibilities. The Ministry of Defence has a Chief Scientist and a Controller Establishments and Research with the exact responsibilities of a Controller R. & D. All Departments accept the customer-contractor principle; but it must be hard for the departmental customer and contractor to understand their respective roles in the Department's R. & D. with such a bewildering array of designations. The confusion is confounded when extra- or inter-departmental relationships are involved.

MULTIFUNCTIONAL LABORATORIES AND INSTITUTES

20. Such laboratories and institutes have programmes for which different customers should be accountable even if the customers are not in the same
R. 21 Department. There is nothing abnormal nor organisationally unsound in

8

such a situation, though some people have difficulty in accepting or becoming acclimatised to it. One of the duties of the Controller R. & D. is to integrate the requirements of these separate programme bosses (the customers) with the overall administration of the laboratory or institute. The acceptance of the concept of the multifunctional laboratory or institute is important.

DIALOGUES

21. No system for the administration and prosecution of applied R. & D. will work efficiently and successfully without a continuing dialogue between the customer, the Chief Scientist, the Controller R. & D. and those concerned with the actual prosecution of the R. & D. In an efficient and successful organisation, all those concerned act and behave as a team in spite of formal accountabilities. Without the accountabilities, however, both efficiency and the probability of success are reduced.

CHAPTER III

THE RESEARCH COUNCILS OF THE DEPARTMENT OF EDUCATION AND SCIENCE (D.E.S.)

EXPENDITURE, HEAD OFFICE STAFF AND MECHANISM OF FINANCIAL SUPPORT

22. There are five Research Councils, the A.R.C., the M.R.C., the N.E.R.C., the Science Research Council (S.R.C.), and the Social Science Research Council (S.S.R.C.). Their expenditure on R. & D., in 1971-72, is given in Table 3, immediately below.

TABLE 3

ESTIMATED NET RESEARCH COUNCIL EXPENDITURE ON R. & D.
1971–72*

	£ million
Science	50·9
Social Science	2·2
Agricultural	18·7
Medical	22·4
Natural Environment	15·3
	109·5

* Excluding the Natural History Museum, £1·7 million (£0·5 million from the D.O.E.) and Grants for Science (including the Royal Societies) £2·0 million.

23. One of the main tasks of the Council for Scientific Policy, also under the D.E.S., is to advise the Secretary of State for Education and Science about the distribution of funds, £109·5 million in 1971-72, between the five Research Councils.

24. The head office organisations of the C.S.P. and the Research Councils consist of 1,078 people (4.6.1971) *and* 116 Council Members (3 vacancies) plus Assessors, together with 128 permanent committees, boards or groups.

9

The cost of the 1,078 whole-time staff will be about £4 million in 1971. A
R. 22 review of these numbers is needed. The C.S.P. and the Research Councils
R. 23 would be well advised to obtain the co-operation of specialists within the Civil
Service Department when conducting this review, which should include a
R. 24 study of the need for the 128 permanent committees, boards and groups.
Much valuable, specialised manpower is tied up in them.

25. In what follows the S.R.C. and S.S.R.C. have not been considered
because the first is largely concerned with pure, and to a lesser extent applied
science, which is not synonymous with research; while the second is in its
R. 25 infancy; but in both cases some applied research is done, and should, accordingly, be studied in due course. This leaves N.E.R.C., the M.R.C. and the
A.R.C. which are discussed below. Before that, however, some general
observations must be made about the Research Councils. The Council for
Scientific Policy, in its role of spokesman for the Research Councils, does not
accept that there is an unambiguous difference between pure and applied
research. It believes that the adjectives pure and applied imply a division
where none should exist and that their use can be harmful. This view is not
easy to understand, if the distinction is made in the terms of paragraph 6
above. It is not of course in dispute that the results of pure research may
sometimes be of applied or practical value, and that applied research may
R. 26 produce results of ' pure ' interest and importance. The Government should,
therefore, reject the view that there is no logical division between pure and
applied research, a view that may be intended to protect the Research Councils
from the imaginary ravages of applied R. & D. users.

R. 27 26. The Research Council Members should have two functions in regard
to the applied R. & D. with which they are concerned: first, to advise the chief
executives of the Research Councils' organisations about the quality of their
scientists, engineers and mathematicians and of their work; and, secondly, to
' protect ' their organisations from hypothetical political or administrative
pressures of an undesirable nature. A number of executive departments, for
example, the Home Office, the Ministry of Defence, the Department of Trade
and Industry and the Department of the Environment have Research Councils
or equivalent bodies, which, though constitutionally different from the D.E.S.
Research Councils, have or should have analogous functions. The independence of such Council Members is an important component of the system.

27. Reference was made above to the ' chief executives of the Research
Councils' organisations '. In D.E.S. Research Council language, they may
be the Secretary or the Chairman. The reader will, doubtless, have realised
that, in the case of the M.R.C., A.R.C. and N.E.R.C., the Secretary's func-
R. 28 tions in respect of applied R. & D. should be identical with those of the
Controller R. & D., see paragraph 12 *et seq.*, page 6 in this report, and it
would be in the interests of clarity and, therefore, efficiency if he were desig-
nated as such. The Secretary of State for Education and Science should obtain
the approval of the Secretaries of State or Ministers of the appropriate executive departments before appointing the chief executives and part-time
Chairmen of the M.R.C., A.R.C. and N.E.R.C., apart from consulting the
President of the Royal Society. In the case of the M.R.C. this implies getting

the approval of the Secretary of State of the Department of Health and Social Security (D.H.S.S.); in the case of the A.R.C., the Minister of Agriculture, Fisheries and Food; in the case of N.E.R.C., the Secretaries of State for Wales and of the D.O.E. and the D.T.I.; and in the case of all three, the Secretary of State for Scotland. R. 29

28. Ultimately and logically, the Chief Executive of the M.R.C. should assume the role of Controller R. & D. in relation to the appropriate experimental work by or on behalf of the D.H.S.S. and S.H.H.D. The same naturally applies to the M.A.F.F. with respect to the A.R.C.[1] The present division is both illogical and undesirable. It perpetuates meaningless or harmful distinctions between research and development, and panders to scientific snobbery—the 'haves' in the Research Councils and the 'have nots' in the Departments.

29. Each Research Council should have a whole-time Secretary, Chief Executive or Controller R. & D., and a part-time Chairman, to obviate what R. 30 is believed to be the inefficient situation mentioned in the second sentence of paragraph 27.

30. A recommendation was made by the Council for Scientific Policy that executive departments should be enabled to place contracts with the Research Councils. This is strongly supported and the recommended size of these contracts is given in Table 4; but the Research Councils should not have R. 31 the right to reject such contracts without good reasons *agreed* with the sponsoring executive department. Some observations must, however, be made: first, the Council for Scientific Policy referred to the executive departments requiring scientific support. They do not require scientific support, but applied R. & D., to achieve specific, pre-determined objectives. Secondly, the Council for Scientific Policy suggested the replacement of the C.S.P. by an executive, chartered body, the Board of Research Councils, one of whose functions would be to ensure that the requirements of executive departments were being properly met. This function is unnecessary except in regard to work quality. Subject to certain reservations discussed later, the executive departments should themselves ensure that they get what they want from the R. 32 Research Councils. If they do not, they can and, doubtless, will go elsewhere, R. 33 with their money, to get their objectives met

31. The recommendations in Table 4 imply a 25 per cent reduction in the D.E.S. vote (the Science Budget) for the Research Councils, and, in the first instance, a corresponding increase in the votes of the appropriate Departments. These recommendations explain and amplify the remark, made immediately above, that the executive departments should themselves ensure that they get what they want from the Research Councils. Nevertheless, the recommendations in the Table are conditional and the conditions are mentioned immediately below. One is that before the recommended changes for the new system of financing the Research Councils are implemented, in principle on

---

[1] The arrangements for applied agricultural R. & D. in Scotland differ from those in England and Wales. The Department of Agriculture and Fisheries for Scotland (D.A.F.S.) already finances the bulk of agricultural research in Scotland, with A.R.C. advice, and also finances three Colleges with R. & D. functions. This difference in existing practice will no doubt be taken into account in discussion of the principles referred to in this Report.

R. 34 5.4.1972, the D.H.S.S. and the M.A.F.F. must have set up Chief Scientist organisations to enable the customers in these two Departments to carry out their new and onerous responsibilities. At the time of writing this report, 16.9.1971, the M.A.F.F.'s Chief Scientist organisation is inadequate and that of the D.H.S.S. is incomplete. That of the D.O.E. is broadly satisfactory and this Department should have no difficulty with its contracts to N.E.R.C.

TABLE 4

RECOMMENDED CHANGES IN THE SYSTEM OF FINANCING
THE D.E.S. RESEARCH COUNCILS AS FROM 5.4.1972, AS IF THE
R. 35 ESTIMATED NET 1971–72 EXPENDITURE, SEE TABLE 3, APPLIED.
(£ million)

(1) Research Council	(2) To be paid by D.E.S. if present system continues	(3) To be paid by D.E.S. under recommended system	(4) To be paid by M.A.F.F., D.H.S.S., D.O.E. or D.T.I. under recommended system
Science	50·9	50·9	0
Social Science	2·2	2·2	0
Agricultural	18·7	4·2	14·5 (M.A.F.F.)
Medical...	22·4	16·8	5·6 (D.H.S.S.)*
Natural Environment ...	15·3	7·7	7·6 (D.O.E.,† 4·0; D.T.I., 3·2; M.A.F.F., 0·4)

* Including the Scottish Home and Health Department (S.H.H.D.).
† Including the Scottish Development Department (S.D.D.).

Notes on Table 4

(i) Some observations on the derivations of the figures relating to the Agricultural, Medical and Natural Environment Research Councils are given in the Appendix, which also contains important recommendations relating to Table 4.

(ii) When discussing the customer–contractor principle in Departments, reference was made to the split between the customer and the Controller R. & D. in respect of capital expenditure. This split would be inappropriate and unmanageable in the case of the Research Councils, which explains why, in Tables 3 and 4, capital and operating expenditure have not been separated.

32. A Chief Scientist organisation does not just consist of a Chief Scientist and, for example, some Advisory Council which may well not be necessary. A Chief Scientist organisation is, as the phrase indicates, an organisation. In the Ministry of Defence, where there is more technical expertise than in several other Departments, which might be held to imply a need for a relatively small Chief Scientist organisation, the Chief Scientific Adviser's organisation in fact consists of more than 50 people.

33. A second condition is that if this recommended change in the financing of the Research Councils is implemented, the amount paid to the Research Councils by the Departments in the first year under the new régime should

not be less than would have been spent if no change had occurred. Further- *R. 36*
more, after this first year, the Departments should not reduce their payments
to the Research Councils by more than 10 per cent per year for three years. *R. 37*
It is, naturally, a matter for the Departments to decide if they wish to increase
their payments to the Research Councils.

34. There is, therefore, a four-year Transition Period. Towards the end
of it, the Departments and the Chief Scientific Adviser to the Government
(see paragraph 57) should review the need for any increase or decrease in the
extent to which the M.R.C., A.R.C. and N.E.R.C. should be directly financed *R. 38*
by the Departments concerned; also whether the 10 per cent rate of reduction
in payments, if it has occurred, should be allowed to continue or not.

35. Because of the rather small size of the D.H.S.S. and S.H.H.D. participation in the M.R.C.'s affairs and because of the intimate relationship
which should exist between these Departments and the M.R.C., the Chief
Medical Officers of the D.H.S.S. and S.H.H.D. should be Members of the
Medical Research Council, *not* only Assessors to the Council. In addition, *R. 39*
both Departments should be represented on those Boards and Committees
of the M.R.C. which are relevant to their interests. Apart from other departmental representation, the Chief Scientists, D.H.S.S., M.A.F.F., D.O.E. and
D.T.I. should, of course, respectively be Members of the M.R.C., A.R.C.
and N.E.R.C., the D.O.E. and the D.T.I. both having a considerable interest *R. 40*
in N.E.R.C. programmes.

36. The composition and duties of the Council for Scientific Policy should *R. 41*
be as follows:

    (*a*) It should have a part-time independent Chairman, appointed by the
        Secretary of State for Education and Science with the agreement of
        the President of the Royal Society;

    (*b*) Its members should consist of an independent Chairman, the five
        Chief Executives or Controllers R. & D. of the Research Councils,
        the Chairman of the University Grants Committee and four eminent,
        independent Scientists, but no Assessors;

    (*c*) It should, as at present, have an extremely small secretariat, provided
        by the D.E.S.;

    (*d*) It should *advise* the Secretary of State about the distribution of
        funds between the Research Councils apart from money provided by
        the Departments or others, with which it will not be concerned.

    Note
    No useful purpose would appear to be served by the President of the
    Royal Society being a Member, first because the President is too
    important, as *ex officio* head of the scientific establishment, to become *R. 42*
    involved in departmental decision-making; and, secondly, because
    it is neither desirable nor possible to distinguish between the President
    as a distinguished scientist and the President as President.

37. The Council for Scientific Policy does not accept that the Research
Councils are concerned with applied R. & D. but with ' strategic and basic
science '. Basic research or science seems to be identical with pure research

or science. Strategic science refers to work in a field of general practical interest, but there is no precise objective specified by a customer, user, or representative of a customer or user. A comment has been made about this type of R. & D., in paragraph 9 (*a*), *Note*, on page 4. ' Tactical science ', which is equated with ' scientific knowledge ', is said to be done by the executive departments but not the Research Councils, except, in the future, under contract, with the Research Councils having the right to refuse to accept contracts. Given that the very names of the Research Councils, Medical, Agricultural, and Natural Environment, obviously imply applications, this philosophy or outlook should be rejected.

RESEARCH COUNCIL UNITS

38. The Research Councils have had the policy of establishing Units, usually but not necessarily at universities and hospitals, centred often on one particularly good scientist; and of closing down the Unit if or when the scientist in question is no longer available. The Research Councils should pay *R. 43* particular attention to the second part of this policy.

' LONGER-TERM ' RESEARCH

39. Anxiety is sometimes expressed about the will or ability of executive departments and industry to engage in longer-term R. & D., which is assumed to refer to an R. & D. project that is expected to last more than five years; and it is said there is a natural tendency for it to be displaced or replaced by short-term or *ad hoc* work. The Universities, the Research Councils and the General Research surcharge exist to counter this tendency when, in an imperfect world, it occurs. Nevertheless, it is the duty of an applied R. & D. administrator to ensure that there is a mix of short, medium and longer-term R. & D. in most of the laboratories under his control, not only because of the intrinsic desirability of the mix, provided the end objectives are clearly specified; but also to gratify the desires of, at any rate, some of the scientists, engineers and mathematicians in the establishments. But longer-term research has no special merit or value in itself, and there is no positive correlation between the importance of a discovery and the time it took to make.

THE ROYAL SOCIETIES GRANT

40. At present this is paid by the D.E.S. Considering the status and role of the Royal Societies in science, engineering and mathematics, both in the United Kingdom and elsewhere, it would seem more appropriate for their grants to be paid centrally, i.e. by the Cabinet Office and the Scottish Office, rather than by a particular Department of State. It is, accordingly, recom- *R. 44* mended that this change should be made as from 5.4.1972, although the Royal Society (London) is satisfied with the present arrangement.

CONTRACTS FROM GOVERNMENT DEPARTMENTS, EXCLUDING THE D.E.S., TO THE RESEARCH COUNCILS

41. All contracts from Government Departments to the Research Councils, or work sponsored by Government Departments and carried out by the *R. 45* Research Councils should, without exception, be paid for by the Government Department in question. When mcre than one Government Department is involved, a decision should be taken by the Government Departments, not

by the Research Councils, as to which Government Department should pay. Little difficulty should be experienced in most cases in deciding which Government Department is the most interested.

42. The reader will remember ' Multifunctional Laboratories ', paragraph 20 on page 8, which is relevant to this subject.

THE PAY OF CHAIRMEN AND MEMBERS OF SOME RESEARCH COUNCILS AND OTHER SCIENTIFIC ADVISORY BODIES

43. It is hard to understand the logic of any system there may be within Government for deciding whether or not independent members of Councils, Boards and Standing Committees should be paid, or give their services free apart from out-of-pocket expenses, Table 5; and it is strongly recommended that this subject be examined, or re-examined, by the Civil Service Department, attention being paid to the duty of the citizen to render public service and to be remunerated with this in mind. The subject is a difficult one because membership of a high-sounding Council, Board, etc. may well be less arduous than that of a comparatively obscure Government Committee.

R. 46

TABLE 5

THE PAY OF CHAIRMEN AND MEMBERS OF SOME RESEARCH COUNCILS AND OTHER SCIENTIFIC ADVISORY BODIES

Body	Chairman	Independent Members
Defence Scientific Advisory Council, M.O.D.	£18·90 per day	£15·75 per day
Home Office Scientific Advisory Council ...	0	0
Noise Advisory Council, D.O.E.	£15·75 per day	£12·60 per day
Advisory Council on Research & Development for Fuel and Power, D.T.I.	0	0
Aeronautical Research Council, D.T.I. ...	£15·75 per day	£12·60 per day
Council for Scientific Policy	£1,500 per year	£15·75 per day
Medical Research Council	£1,000 per year	£750 per year

CHAPTER IV

SCIENTISTS, ENGINEERS AND MATHEMATICIANS IN THE CIVIL SERVICE AND THEIR MOVEMENTS

44. Reference was made in paragraph 14 to the responsibility of the Controller R. & D. for ensuring an adequate, systematic and continuing flow of people out of and into research establishments. It is, therefore, of interest to study the present situation. The following table shows the number of senior

Grade	Number in grade	Number with S.E.M. degrees	Percentage
Permanent Secretary	28	3	11
Deputy Secretary	82	13	16
Under-Secretary	304	33	11
Assistant Secretary	824	72	9
Principal	1,086	118	11
Assistant Principal	325	40	12

civil servants in the former Administrative Class with degrees in science, engineering or mathematics (S.E.M.) on 30.4.1971.

The rather low percentage of ex-scientists, mathematicians and engineers among senior administrative civil servants may be due to the almost complete lack of movement from the Scientific Civil Service into the Administrative Class. Only 36 former members of the Scientific Civil Service have moved over to the Administrative Class, and although the majority of these were transferred in comparatively recent years, the annual rate of movement is small. The number of transfers to and from the United Kingdom Atomic Energy Authority and the Medical Research Council was equally low. While the paucity of technically qualified people within the Administrative Class of the Civil Service may cause some despondency, the virtually complete immobility of the Scientific Civil Service is, or shortly will become, a major national problem. The immobility of the Scientific Civil Service has been eased in recent years by the introduction of so-called ' opportunity posts ' in headquarters organisations; this is all to the good and should be encouraged. The vitality and efficiency of a laboratory depends on an adequate flow of scientists, mathematicians and engineers through it, apart from that which occurs through retirement and recruitment; and it is one important function of the research administrator, the Controller R. & D., to ensure that this flow takes place. If he is prevented from discharging this function, someone else must take the blame for the undesirably skewed age distributions which result *R. 47* from this policy. As a start in the rectification of this organisational failure, the quality of management at the higher levels of the Scientific Civil Service should be improved by insisting that no-one should be appointed Director or Deputy Director of a Laboratory or Institute unless he or she has had a spell of at least one year in the Department's headquarters in London, preferably on the administrative side. The acquisition of administrative experience at a fairly early age is also necessary to enable scientists to make their proper contribution in policy-making posts at headquarters.

R. 48 45. Equally, there is no *a priori* reason why an Under-Secretary or Deputy Secretary should not become the Director of a large Government Laboratory, Institute or Establishment, for a period of years. The larger the undertaking, the less critical the Director's technical training becomes. It is administrative ability that counts in such cases.

46. It may be of interest to compare what is said above with the views of the Fulton Committee about scientists and other specialists in the Civil Service. The Committee expressed the view that:

  (a) the specialist classes (architects, lawyers, doctors, engineers, scientists, accountants, economists, draughtsmen, technicians and so on) did not get the responsibility, authority and opportunities they ought to have;

  (b) there should be an open road to the top of the Service for all kinds of talent and an open structure in the top management posts;

  (c) suitable specialists at the lower and middle levels of the Service should be employed outside their own specialisation;

  (d) there should be greater mobility between the Civil Service and other employment.

47. The Committee concluded that:

(*a*) all classes should be abolished and replaced by a single unified grading structure covering all civil servants from top to bottom in the non-industrial part of the Service, the correct grading of each post being determined by job evaluation;

(*b*) specialists should receive more training in management and opportunities for greater responsibility and wider careers, e.g., in policy formulation and financial control;

(*c*) in some of the big technical departments there might be a need for a further senior post; a Chief Scientist, engineer or other specialist.

48. The programme of work jointly agreed by the Official and Staff Sides following the Fulton Report has had the following results to date:

(*a*) Unified grading is to be applied to all posts of Under Secretary level and above, and the aim is to complete this process in about six months time;

(*b*) The Administrative, Executive and Clerical Classes up to Assistant Secretary level have been amalgamated to form the Administration Group of the new General Category; the former Economist and Statistician Classes at these levels have been replaced by occupational groups within the General Category;

(*c*) The Scientific Classes up to the level of Principal Scientific Officer have been amalgamated to form the new Science Category; consultations continue on a projected merger of the Works Group and Associated Classes to form a third major category;

(*d*) Freer movement between specialisations and into general management has already been achieved. Proposals for improved career management of specialists—including their development for top posts—are being worked out. These include arrangements for identifying, at about Principal level, professionals who would benefit from experience in administrative and managerial posts. Management training for specialist staff has been introduced and is being extended.

Advantage should be taken of these changes greatly to accelerate the flow of Scientists from departmental research to other work in the Civil Service. The *R. 49* best scientists should be encouraged to gain administrative experience early in their careers, but satisfactory progress in this matter will only be achieved if it attracts the full support of Ministers and top management, including the present generation of senior scientists. It is not enough just to offer the opportunity. The good scientist will be unwilling to risk his research career without positive assurance that the acquisition of administrative experience will be regarded as a positive asset in a career leading to senior posts in the scientific field as well as outside it.

CHAPTER V

THE 'HALDANE PRINCIPLE'

49. This 'Principle' is sometimes invoked to justify the independence of applied scientists from those who may benefit from the results of their work.

Before accepting this concept, it is worth studying what the Haldane Committee[1] actually said, particularly since more than 50 years have elapsed since it was set up. The Haldane Committee found that Government would, in general, be better able to formulate policy if more facts, information and research facilities were available to Government decision makers. Certain Government Departments, namely the Departments of the Army and Navy, already benefited from such services.

50. The Committee recommended that the Departments of the Central Government should be divided according to the services they rendered to the community as a whole. One such service was the provision of research and information.

51. There were three different levels of Government research:

(a) research done in administrative Departments;

(b) research supervised by administrative Departments; and

(c) research done for the use of all Departments.

52. Research for general Government use had several functions:

(a) to keep Ministers informed;

(b) to carry out investigations in response, for example, to questions in the House of Commons (and the need for Government answers);

(c) to make sure that the Government kept in touch with scientific workers in different parts of the country;

(d) to enquire, without (sic) implementing findings; and

(e) to carry out enquiries the result of which would be useful to different Departments.

53. The Committee could not predict in which direction research would progress, but it anticipated that a separate Department of intelligence and research would eventually be established with its own Minister.

54. The concepts of scientific independence used in the Haldane Report are not relevant to contemporary discussion of Government research. The Report argued that a Government research Department should be *administratively* independent of other Government Departments; but so far as the *content* of research programmes was concerned, the committee used two distinct concepts of Government research. First, it argued that Central Government research should serve different Departments and help them in the formulation of policy, as in functions (a)–(e) in paragraph 52. These limited functions of Government research are not controversial, either in 1918 or now. Secondly, the Report asserted that Government research should serve the community as a whole; but, in fact, the Report mentions only such 'community-serving' research activities as follow directly from specific and formulated Government policies. The specific policies mentioned in the Report are of great generality and little contemporary use: to promote an

---

[1] Report on the Machinery of Government, Cd. 9230, 14.12.1918.

increase of material production; to promote the health of the entire community; and to apply science to industry.

55. From what is said above it is clear that there is no single ' Haldane Principle '; but the following sentence from the Haldane Committee's Report is sometimes quoted, out of context, to justify ' scientific independence ':

> ' It [the recommended structure] places responsibility to Parliament in the hands of a Minister who is . . . immune from any suspicion of being biased by administrative considerations against the application of the results of research.'

The question of administrative independence is not central to the customer-contractor principle; but if this sentence implies that the application of the results of research should be the responsibility of the independent scientific Ministry, it should have been unacceptable in 1918 and must be now. The further implication that the objectives that require applied R. & D. for their achievement should be formulated by this independent Ministry, Department, Council or Committee is, of course, entirely unrealistic. The ' Haldane Principle ' has, evidently, little or no bearing on the conduct and management of Government R. & D. in the '70s.

CHAPTER VI

THE CHIEF SCIENTIFIC ADVISER

56. In June 1971, the Chief Scientific Adviser's inherited staff consisted, including himself, of four physicists, two mathematicians, one engineer and one economist. If this organisation is to exercise any form of oversight of trans-departmental and trans-national science, this distribution of disciplines needs revision. There should be one chemist (preferably a physical chemist) and one life scientist within the Chief Scientific Adviser's organisation. This *R. 50* does not imply that the staff should be proportionately increased, though this could be done by secondment.

INTER-DEPARTMENTAL CO-ORDINATION

57. There is a danger that R. & D. done by one Department may have an impact on that done elsewhere or by another Department, but that the latter will not know about the work of the former. The avoidance of this danger is a matter for the Chief Scientific Adviser and implies both a knowledge of the programmes and budgets of the principal laboratories or institutes supported by the Departments, and of research projects that will become expensive in the development phase and that may compete with, or have a bearing on, analogous projects in another Department. The Advanced Passenger Train and the Tracked Hovercraft projects would be a case in point, were it not for the fact that the former got to the development stage much earlier than the latter. It is recommended that such inter-departmental co-ordination and *R. 51* compilation of information should be clearly understood to be the responsibility of the Chief Scientific Adviser. The successful compilation and co-ordination of such information also involves knowledge of industrial R. & D. projects. This task, of the Chief Scientific Adviser, is a major and continuing

one whose successful prosecution will greatly improve the efficiency of Government R. & D.

58. Reference has been made elsewhere in this report, see, for example, page 2, to the feeling many people have that advantages accrue from there being some central body whose duty is to exercise ' general oversight' of Government and, even, national R. & D. So far as pure or fundamental research is concerned, this oversight is exercised by the Research Councils, particularly the Science Research Council, and the Council for Scientific Policy. So far as applied R. & D. is concerned, the inescapable conclusion from this report is that general oversight would serve no useful purpose and, indeed, would negate the principles put forward in the report.

59. Reference has, however, been made to the Chief Scientific Adviser's co-ordinating role when projects involving R. & D. in one Department have an impact elsewhere. There is nothing to stop the Chief Scientific Adviser setting up *ad hoc* committees to deal with such situations or, indeed, others; R. 52 and it is strongly recommended that this system be used rather than set up yet another scientific advisory organisation, unless events in the future make it desirable to reconsider this question.

COMMENT

60. The recommendations made in this report cannot be implemented overnight. Many of them involve changes in attitude, orientation and procedure which will take time to accept, let alone digest. Their implementation R. 53 should, therefore, be monitored and reported on by the Chief Scientific Adviser to the Government.

APPENDIX

INTERPRETATION OF TABLE 4

D.H.S.S., S.H.H.D.-M.R.C.

(i) The interaction between the D.H.S.S. and S.H.H.D. and the M.R.C. has, so far, been inadequate and the changes recommended in Table 4 and elsewhere are intended to rectify this deficiency. At present, although the D.H.S.S. and S.H.H.D. have direct responsibilities in the field of public health, they have no share, as of right, in M.R.C. decisions and cannot be certain of always being consulted about the M.R.C.'s work on, for example, nutrition, toxicology, vaccines and blood transfusion. The same applies to clinical medicine, despite the direct responsibility of D.H.S.S. and S.H.H.D. for the N.H.S.; to cancer and radiation; to ageing (on which the M.R.C. spent £9,000 in 1970–71); to cardio-vascular disease, renal disorders and rheumatism; to endocrinology, psychiatry and psychology, neurology (special senses), and occupational health. The same applies to epidemiology and social medicine. In the light of these factors a good case could be made for transferring to the D.H.S.S. and, where relevant, the S.H.H.D. about £11 million out of the D.E.S. total for the M.R.C. of £22·4 million (1971–72); but in the first instance, the recommended transfer has been reduced from this value to £5·6 million, Table 4, *as if* the changes were to take place in 1971–72. In 1972–73, the D.E.S. total for the M.R.C. and the corresponding transfer to the D.H.S.S. and S.H.H.D. will be proportionately greater and this naturally applies to other cases mentioned in this Appendix and in Table 4.

M.A.F.F., D.A.F.S.-A.R.C.

(ii) The reason why it is recommended that only £14·5 million of the D.E.S. total of £18·7 million for the A.R.C. should be transferred to the M.A.F.F. is as follows: the A.R.C. will spend about £1·3 million[1] in 1971–72 on its Units. Most of their work is long-term and some, for example the study of the mechanism of muscular contraction, of questionable relevance to agriculture. This does not, of course, mean that such work is uninteresting; nor that it should not be done. Three Institutes, the Animal Breeding Research Organisation (£0·6 million), the Institute of Animal Physiology (£1 million), and the Letcombe Laboratory (£0·3 million) should also continue to be financed by the A.R.C. Their programmes come into the category of what is sometimes called ' strategic research ', i.e. research in a field of agricultural interest, but without an applied objective which is likely to be realised in a specified time, however long. Some observations about this type of research are made in paragraph 9 (a) *Note*, on page 4. The Soil Survey of England and Wales (£0·2 million) should continue to be financed by the A.R.C., and the corresponding Scottish survey by D.A.F.S., pending the results of a study, which it is recommended should be made, of its relationship *R. 54*

---

[1] This and other figures in this section have been rounded off, which explains minor discrepancies between them and those in Table 4.

with the work of N.E.R.C. in general, the Institute of Geological Sciences and the Experimental Cartography Unit in particular, and with the Department of the Environment. Such a study would, it is hoped, lead, *inter alia*, to organisational recommendations.

(iii) A proportion of the work of the John Innes Institute (£0·2 million) and of Rothamsted Experimental Station (£0·5 million) should continue to be paid for by the A.R.C. because these amounts fall in the basic or strategic research category.

D.O.E., D.T.I., M.A.F.F., D.A.F.S., S.D.D.-N.E.R.C.

(iv) The recommendations affecting the N.E.R.C. are slightly more complicated than those relating to the M.R.C. and A.R.C., because of the heterogeneity of the subjects embraced by N.E.R.C. But the recommendations are in no sense intrinsically complicated provided attention is paid to the customer-contractor principle and the concept of the multifunctional laboratory or institute.

(v) The N.E.R.C. programme is divided into work related to the Earth, the Oceans and Seas, Inland Waters and the Countryside. To give an example as to how the N.E.R.C. financial transfers recommended in Table 4 were arrived at, two items from N.E.R.C.'s Earth programme are mentioned immediately below, with comments:

' *Mineral Resources:* To undertake scientific reconnaissance and assess the potential of mineral deposits.'

Comment: The D.T.I. is the sponsoring Department for the minerals industry (except sand and gravel). It also has a statutory responsibility for all mineral extraction.

'*Underground Water:* To determine ground-water conditions and evaluate underground water resources, including underground storage and transport.'

Comment: The D.O.E. and S.D.D. are the sponsoring Departments for the water industry.

The Oceans and Seas provide a different example:

' *Biological Resources of the Sea:* To study transmission through food chains to useable resources of fish, shellfish and sea mammals; optimum conditions for growth and nutrition.'

Comment: This work should be sponsored by the M.A.F.F. and/or D.A.F.S.

R. 55

Inland Waters contains such projects as ' Water balance of catchments ', ' River régimes ' and ' Pollution of inland waters ', which should be paid for by the D.O.E. Exceptionally, the Institute of Hydrology should be physically transferred, together with its staff, to the D.O.E., where it should be fused with the D.O.E.'s contiguous Hydraulics Research Station. The whole of the Countryside programme should be financed by the D.O.E. and S.D.D., which explains why the Nature Conservancy (excluding basic ecological research (£0·25 million)) should be paid for by these Departments.

22

SUMMARY OF RECOMMENDATIONS

R. 1	Application of customer-contractor principle to all applied research and development.
R. 2–8	Responsibilities of the Customer.
R. 9	Role of the Chief Scientist.
R. 10–15	Responsibilities of the Controller R. & D.
R. 16–19	Function and operation of the General Research Surcharge.
R. 20	Chief Scientist—Controller R. & D. terminology to be adopted by all Departments with significant applied R. & D. programmes, except for the D.E.S. and, for the time being, the Home Office.
R. 21	Acceptance of the multifunctional laboratory or institute concept.
R. 22–23	Review of D.E.S. Research Councils' Head Office numbers.
R. 24	Review of number of D.E.S. Research Council permanent committees.
R. 25	Study, in due course, of activities of the S.S.R.C.
R. 26	View that there is no logical distinction between pure and applied research to be rejected.
R. 27	Functions of D.E.S. Research Council Members in regard to applied R. & D.
R. 28	Functions of D.E.S. Research Council chief executives in regard to applied R. & D.
R. 29	Approval of appropriate Secretaries of State or Ministers needed before appointing chief executives or part-time chairmen of the M.R.C., A.R.C., and N.E.R.C.
R. 30	Each Research Council to have a whole-time chief executive and part-time Chairman.
R. 31	D.E.S. Research Councils not to have right to reject contracts from Departments without good reasons agreed with the sponsoring Department.
R. 32–33	Right of the Departments to contract work to organisations other than the D.E.S. Research Councils.
R. 34	Need for satisfactory Chief Scientist organisations in the M.A.F.F. and D.T.I. before financial transfers are made from the D.E.S. to them.
R. 35	Financial transfers, amounting to £27·7 million, from the D.E.S. to the M.A.F.F., D.H.S.S., D.O.E., D.T.I., S.H.H.D. and S.D.D.
R. 36–37	Conditions on which the implementation of R. 35 is dependent.
R. 38	Implementation of R. 35 to be monitored by Chief Scientific Adviser.
R. 39–40	Representatives of the appropriate Departments to be M.R.C., A.R.C. and N.E.R.C. Council Members.
R. 41–42	Functions and composition of the Council for Scientific Policy.
R. 43	Useful life-span of D.E.S. Research Council Units needs special attention.

R. 44   Royal Societies' annual grant to be paid by Cabinet Office and Scottish Office.

R. 45   All work done by D.E.S. Research Councils on behalf of Departments to be paid for by the latter.

R. 46   Examination, by C.S.D., of pay of Chairmen and Members of Scientific Advisory bodies and all departmental Research Councils.

R. 47   Directors and deputy directors of laboratories to have head office experience before being appointed.

R. 48   Senior members of the former Administrative Class eligible to become directors of large institutes.

R. 49   Flow of scientists out of departmental Research Functions into other parts of the Civil Serivce to be greatly accelerated.

R. 50   More scientific disciplines to be represented in the Chief Scientific Adviser's office.

R. 51   Inter-departmental co-ordination of R. & D. to be the responsibility of the Chief Scientific Adviser.

R. 52   No other scientific advisory organisation is needed for inter-departmental co-ordination of R. & D.

R. 53   Chief Scientific Adviser to monitor R. 1–52 and R. 54–55.

R. 54   Special examination, with recommendations, of the relationship between the Soil Survey of England and Wales, the Institute of Geological Sciences, the Experimental Cartography Unit, and the D.O.E.

R. 55   Physical transfer of Institute of Hydrology, and its staff, to D.O.E., followed by fusion with Hydraulics Research Station.

ACKNOWLEDGMENT

The advice and help of those listed below is gratefully acknowledged

Mr. W. O. Campbell Adamson, Confederation of British Industry
Sir Douglas Allen, K.C.B., Treasury
Sir Philip Allen, G.C.B., Home Office
Sir William Armstrong, G.C.B., M.V.O., Civil Service Department
The Hon. J. J. Astor, M.B.E., D.L., J.P., Agricultural Research Council
Dr. H. H. Atkinson, Cabinet Office
Sir Kenneth Berrill, K.C.B., University Grants Committee
Mr. R. J. H. Beverton, C.B.E., M.A., Natural Environment Research Council
Professor H. Bondi, F.R.A.S., F.R.S., Ministry of Defence
Mr. A. R. Bunker, C.B., Home Office
Dr. R. Cohen, Department of Health and Social Security
Mr. F. Cooper, C.B., C.M.G., Civil Service Department
Sir Alan Cottrell, F.R.S., Cabinet Office
Sir Gordon Cox, F.R.S., Agricultural Research Council
Professor Sir Frederick Dainton, F.R.S., Council for Scientific Policy
Dr. Duncan S. Davies, Imperial Chemical Industries Ltd.
Sir James Dunnett, G.C.B., C.M.G., Ministry of Defence
Sir Basil Engholm, K.C.B., Ministry of Agriculture, Fisheries and Food
Professor Sir Brian Flowers, F.R.S., Science Research Council
Mr. D. J. Gerhard, Civil Service Department
Sir George Godber, G.C.B., D.M., F.R.C.P., Department of Health and Social
    Security
Dr. J. A. B. Gray, Medical Research Council
Sir Douglas Haddow, K.C.B., Scottish Office
Professor A. L. Hodgkin, P.R.S.
Lord Kearton, F.R.S., Courtaulds Ltd.
Mr. D. J. Lyons, B.Sc., F.R.Ae.S., Department of the Environment
Mr. W. McCall, Institute of Professional Civil Servants
Dr. I. Maddock, C.B., O.B.E., F.R.S., Department of Trade and Industry
Mr. W. A. C. Mathieson, C.B., C.M.G., M.B.E., Overseas Development Adminis-
    tration (F.C.O.)
Mr. N. G. Morrison, Civil Service Department
The Duke of Northumberland, K.G., F.R.S., Medical Research Council
Sir Antony Part, K.C.B., M.B.E., Department of Trade and Industry
Sir William Pile, K.C.B., M.B.E., Department of Education and Science
Mr. L. Pliatzky, Treasury
Mr. D. G. Rayner, Ministry of Defence
Mr. W. K. Reid, Department of Education and Science
Sir Philip Rogers, K.C.B., C.M.G., Department of Health and Social Security
The Royal Society
Mr. W. Rudoe, Department of Health and Social Security
Sir David Serpell, K.C.B., C.M.G., O.B.E., Department of the Environment
Mr. A. A. Shonfield, Social Science Research Council
Dr. O. Simpson, Cabinet Office
Mr. C. J. Stephens, B.Sc., F.I.E.E., F.R.Ae.S., i.d.c., Home Office
Sir Burke Trend, G.C.B., C.V.O., Cabinet Office
Professor V. C. Wynne-Edwards, D.Sc., F.R.S., Natural Environment Research
    Council

A great debt is owed to the Select Committee on Science and Technology for having
ventilated and illuminated so many of the problems discussed in this report.

THE FUTURE OF THE
RESEARCH COUNCIL SYSTEM

REPORT OF A C.S.P. WORKING GROUP
UNDER THE CHAIRMANSHIP OF
SIR FREDERICK DAINTON

COUNCIL FOR SCIENTIFIC POLICY

May 1971

DEAR SECRETARY OF STATE,

FUTURE OF THE RESEARCH COUNCIL SYSTEM

I enclose the report of a Working Group of the Council for Scientific Policy on the future of the Research Council system.

As the body appointed to advise you on your Department's scientific responsibilities, we welcome this opportunity to make a general review of the Research Council system. Throughout our enquiry we have borne in mind the stated intention of the Government to review the whole of its Research and Development effort and we hope that, in addition to being of use to you in a narrower context, this report will be of further use when that appraisal is carried out.

Criticisms have been levelled against the Research Council system which we have taken into account during our work and in the drafting of our recommendations. In particular we have sought to devise an organisational structure for the system which incorporates the important advantages of the present system and which would also enable the Research Councils to play a still more effective part in making progress towards national goals.

In the course of our work we have identified some problems which require clear and more protracted examination. We consider that one of the features of our proposal is that it provides a mechanism by which such problems could be discussed and resolved.

The Council believes that the future of the Research Councils is of great importance and hopes that you will agree to the report's publication to facilitate wide discussion.

Yours sincerely,

(*Signed*) FREDERICK DAINTON.

The Rt. Hon. Mrs. Margaret Thatcher, M.P.

' And having thus endeavoured to discharge our duties in this weighty affair...and to approve our sincerity therein (so far as lay in us) to the consciences of all men; although we know it impossible (in such variety of apprehensions, humours and interests, as are in the world) to please all; nor can expect that men of factious, peevish, and perverse spirits should be satisfied with anything that can be done in this kind by any other than themselves: Yet we have good hope, that what is here presented, and hath been... with great diligence examined and approved, will be also well accepted and approved by all sober, peaceable and truly conscientious...sons. '

Book of Common Prayer

1662 Preface

Contents

I INTRODUCTION

1. We were appointed by the Council for Scientific Policy (C.S.P.) and with the approval of the Secretary of State in October 1970

' to advise the Secretary of State, through the Council for Scientific Policy, on the most effective arrangements for organising and supporting pure and applied scientific research and postgraduate training.'

The membership of our Group was

Sir FREDERICK DAINTON, F.R.S. (Chairman)
Dr. T. L. COTTRELL
Dr. J. C. KENDREW, F.R.S.
Dr. P. E. KENT, F.R.S.
Dr. A. W. MERRISON, F.R.S.

SECRETARIAT

Mr. R. EDMONDS
Mr. M. J. G. SMITH

We met on 18 days.

Professor F. H. Stewart, F.R.S. who will cease to be a member of the C.S.P. on his appointment as Chairman of N.E.R.C. on 1 October 1971 has not been a member of the Group but has been associated with its work throughout, and we have benefited greatly from his experience and advice.

II WHY THE C.S.P. UNDERTOOK THE ENQUIRY

2. The immediate cause of our appointment was the proposal to transfer the Agricultural Research Council to the Ministry of Agriculture, Fisheries and Food. This proposal had not previously been discussed with the C.S.P. who felt that no sufficient case had been made for what appeared to them to be a fundamental and ill-advised change.

3. Furthermore, nearly six years had elapsed since the C.S.P. was set up and it seemed an appropriate time to consider how the Research Council–C.S.P. system had evolved. During this period the annual growth rate of the Science Budget of the D.E.S. had declined from 12 per cent to 4½ per cent. In 1970 it became clear that it would decline further, whereas the demands on the Research Councils from Government, universities and the general public seemed likely to continue to increase.

4. Finally, the Government announced in October 1970 its intention to review all its research and development activities and it seemed to the C.S.P. that our own enquiry would be essential to that review. The C.S.P. therefore proposed to the Secretary of State that this enquiry should be made, and she

welcomed it both in relation to the work of her own department and as a contribution to the wider Governmental appraisal of its research and development activities.

III PROCEDURE ADOPTED

5. The need to present a report within a short period of time has constrained us to work with only a limited number of consultants. We have discussed with the chief officers of the Agricultural Research Council (A.R.C.), the Medical Research Council (M.R.C.), the Natural Environment Research Council (N.E.R.C.) and the Science Research Council (S.R.C.), the way in which the Research Council system works and possible improvements to it. To assist us in this the Councils prepared at our request detailed analyses of their programmes of work which are presented in an abbreviated form at Appendix C. The Social Science Research Council (S.S.R.C.), which has now come under the aegis of the C.S.P. and the Chairman of which has attended C.S.P. meetings as an assessor for the past two years, was not subjected to a systematic examination, but we have had regard to the functions of the S.S.R.C. in our consideration of the general question of the future management of science, and have been able to take account of the views of the Chairman of the S.S.R.C. We have also had views from officials of the Department of Education and Science, from the Chairman of the University Grants Committee and from other members of the C.S.P. including the President of the Royal Society. We have taken account of unsolicited written evidence from several interested parties including members of Research Council staff and university research workers.

IV SCIENCE AND THE NATION

6. Science is a means of obtaining knowledge about the structure and characteristics of the animate and inanimate world, and its importance to human society is that such knowledge lies at the base of nearly all human activities that influence positively or negatively the quality of human life and its environment. Science makes major contributions to the improvement of health; to the provision of good food, shelter, transport and communication; to the efficient use and conservation of natural resources and the maintenance of a good physical environment; to education; and to the development and maintenance of an internationally competitive industry leading to a healthy economy. It is because governments are aware of the power of science to serve national goals that they are prepared to provide substantial national resources[1] to sustain scientific activities over and above those which any civilised society must provide to allow responsive and creative individuals to advance knowledge in any sphere.

7. The determination of a national policy for science involves many diverse judgments, but most of these are concerned with two broad aims; first, to assess and arrive at a reasonable consensus on various arguments concerning the amount of governmental support that should be provided for science, and second, to ensure that the arrangements for its disposal and use

[1] For details of support of research and development in the U.K. in the period 1961–71 see Appendix D.

will enable the nation to be well served by science. In examining the work cf the Research Councils the many national objectives to which science is relevant have therefore been constantly in our minds. In order to understand the relationships between the objectives and the work which needs to be carried out it is necessary to consider the nature of scientific activity, the people who engage in it and how these are organised.

8. The most important elements in science are the content of attested facts and the theories which give it form and structure and which facilitate further advances. Engineering is commonly thought of as being concerned with the conception, design, and construction of a machine, a structure or a process to achieve some well-defined purpose, such as the conversion of chemical energy into electrical energy. Some would distinguish technology as contributing particularly to the improvement and control of manufacture and of the products of industry. These distinctions are often not very useful and lead to popular misconceptions which can be damaging. There is still a tendency to classify engineers and technologists as ' applied ' scientists. The adjectives ' pure ' and ' applied ' imply a division where none should exist and their use can be harmful. In the course of his work the engineer or technologist makes use of experiment and theory in just the same way as the ' pure ' scientist, and at least as great demands are likely to be put upon his intelligence, judgment and imagination. Moreover, advances in knowledge or improvements in the use of any one of ' pure science ' or ' engineering ' or ' technology ' depend enormously on progress in the other two. In this report we use ' scientist ' to include also engineer and technologist, and ' science ' to include, as well as research, development and teaching activities in science, engineering and technology.

9. The historical boundaries of scientific disciplines are becoming increasingly blurred. Multi- and inter-disciplinary studies grow apace and as a result old boundaries dissolve and the links between seemingly disparate parts grow stronger. This internal cohesion of science is one of its most characteristic features and will surely increase rather than diminish.

10. Rather than adopt any classification by subject or into ' pure ' and ' applied ' we have found it useful to have in our minds the following 3 categories of scientific work

    (*a*) tactical science—the science and its application and development needed by departments of state and by industry to further their immediate executive or commercial functions. The extent and nature of this activity may vary widely according to the functions served and to the degree that they involve science. At one extreme it may contain a significant element of sophisticated research over a long period; whilst at the other extreme it amounts to little more than a modest intelligence and advisory activity;

    (*b*) strategic science—the broad spread of more general scientific effort which is needed as a foundation for this tactical science. It is no less relevant in terms of practical objectives of the sort we have mentioned, but more wide ranging. For this ' strategic ' work to be successful it is necessary to maintain the vigour of the underlying scientific disciplines and to deploy these disciplines with due regard to national goals;

(c) basic science—research and training which have no specific application in view but which are necessary to ensure the advance of scientific knowledge and the maintenance of a corps of able scientists, upon which depends the future ability of the country to use science.

These wide-ranging scientific activities are carried out by people who are employed in public and private industry, in Government Departments, in Research Councils and in higher education.

11. Moreover, in order that research may be carried quickly to the point at which it can be applied and that scientifically trained men and women may be employed to the best advantage, it is important that channels of communications between scientists engaged on basic, strategic and tactical research should not be impeded and that there should be no hindrance to any desirable movement of people between these three types of work.

12. It is important to emphasise that the boundaries between these three categories are not always sharply defined. Basic and strategic science are especially closely linked both with one another and with the higher educational system. A large contribution to research and to the education of future scientists is made by academic staff in science-based university departments (numbering over 15,000 in 1968). The ' users ' of scientific knowledge and of scientists also need to have close connections with basic and strategic science as well as with tactical science. ' Users ' are often thought of merely in terms of employers, for example, science-based industry and Government departments. The category is of course, much wider than this and includes, directly, many self-employed persons, such as doctors, veterinary surgeons, farmers, architects and consultant engineers, and indirectly, the whole community.

V THE PRESENT RESEARCH COUNCIL SYSTEM

A. HISTORY

13. The C.S.P. is now concerned with the 5 Research Councils: Agricultural Research Council (A.R.C.), founded in 1931, Medical Research Council (M.R.C.), originally set up in 1913 and incorporated under its present title in 1920, Natural Environment Research Council (N.E.R.C.), Science Research Council (S.R.C.) and Social Science Research Council (S.S.R.C.), all 3 established in 1965. This system derives from the Science and Technology Act 1965 which was based on some of the recommendations of the Trend Committee (Cmnd. 2171).[1] The relevant recommendations of this Committee were that:

(i) there should be no major change in the functions of the Medical Research Council and the Agricultural Research Council;

(ii) a new Science Research Council should be established for the support of research projects in pure and applied science, including nuclear

---

[1] The Social Science Research Council (S.S.R.C.) was established under the Science and Technology Act 1965 on the recommendations of the Heyworth Committee (Cmnd. 2660), and has only this year come under the aegis of the C.S.P.

science and space research, and that it should assume direct control over the Royal Observatories; but responsibility for the Meteorological Office should remain with the Air Ministry (now Ministry of Defence);

(iii) a new Natural Resources Research Council should be established to be responsible for the work of the Nature Conservancy, the Geological Survey and the Soil Surveys and for research into long-term forestry, oceanography, hydrology, fisheries and related aspects of aquatic biology;

(iv) the system whereby the financing of the main body of scientific research in the universities was shared between the University Grants Committee and the Research Councils should be maintained;

(v) there should be a new body to advise the Minister for Science on all aspects of his responsibilities in relation to civil scientific research.

B. THE WORK OF THE RESEARCH COUNCILS

14. The Research Councils are autonomous bodies, incorporated by Royal Charter and receiving from the Secretary of State for Education and Science under the 1965 Act grants-in-aid which account for almost all their income. Broadly their purpose is to foster research and training in the fields specified in their Charters and they operate flexibly in many ways, including the following:

(i) by the provision of grants to support work undertaken in university departments and in other higher educational establishments, usually for specified periods of up to 3 years but occasionally long-term. These grants can provide the university or college investigator with assistants at any level from technician to post-doctoral research worker and can finance the purchase and maintenance of equipment. They may be used to establish ' groups ' in order to initiate the development of research and teaching in a new field;

(ii) by the provision of maintenance awards and fees to support students who proceed to further studies or training in research after their first degree. About half the British postgraduate students in science are supported in this way. The Councils also provide research training support grants to university departments in respect of holders of such research training awards;

(iii) by the establishment of units, generally in a university or comparable environment, where most of the staff are employed by the Council usually on short-term contract; their directors may be Research Council employees or may be appointed on an honorary basis from among the salaried staff of a university;

(iv) by the provision of expensive experimental facilities used by university research workers, such as the Rutherford and Daresbury high energy physics laboratories of the S.R.C., and of other facilities for the use of both Universities and Council Institutes, such as the research vessels of the N.E.R.C.;

(v) by means of grants to independent research agencies, laboratories and institutes. Examples of these are the Institute of Cancer Research which derives just over 40 per cent of its budget from M.R.C. funds, institutes such as the Rothamsted Experimental Station grant-aided by the A.R.C. and associations such as the Marine Biological Association grant-aided by the N.E.R.C., where the Research Councils provide almost 100 per cent of the independent bodies' budgets;

(vi) by carrying out their own research programmes in their own research institutions and component bodies (which may also provide research facilities for researchers from outside). Examples are the M.R.C. National Institute for Medical Research, the N.E.R.C. Institute of Geological Sciences and A.R.C. Institutes such as the Institute of Animal Physiology, where the research workers are the full-time employees of the Council concerned; and

(vii) by participation in international scientific projects providing facilities for U.K. researchers, such as the European Organisation for Nuclear Research (C.E.R.N.).

15. The degree of detailed administration of research policies exercised by the Research Councils varies considerably according to circumstances but great importance is rightly attached to the encouragement of good ideas generated by individual scientists. For this reason a large element in the policy of the Research Councils has been and will continue to be to support projects on scientific merit in terms of timeliness and promise. However, the Research Councils do not merely react to individual proposals put to them but, after consultation with those concerned, choose for particular support areas which they judge to be of national importance. Additionally in some fields and for a whole variety of reasons, including that of expense, they have found it necessary to encourage the concentration of activity and resources. By these means the Councils seek to maintain the supply of highly-trained manpower at the right level and to develop their fields of responsibility in the national interest.

16. The Research Councils have links with and provide advice and services to a remarkably wide range of Ministries and other public bodies as well as to industry. This is shown clearly in the Research Councils' analyses of their activities (see Appendix C) and a list of the major links is given in Table 1.

TABLE 1

RESEARCH COUNCILS:
SUMMARY OF LINKS WITH WORK
OF OTHER PUBLIC ORGANISATIONS

A.R.C.

Building Research Station (Department of the Environment)
Commonwealth Agricultural Bureaux
Department of Agriculture and Fisheries, Scotland
Food Research Associations
Forestry Commission
Home-Grown Cereals Authority
Hop Marketing Board
Ministry of Agriculture, Fisheries and Food
Meat and Livestock Commission

TABLE 1—*continued*

Milk Marketing Board
National Institute of Agricultural Botany
Public Health Laboratory Service
Potato Marketing Board
River Authorities
Road Research Laboratory
United Kingdom Co-ordinating Committee for Food, Science and Technology
Water Pollution Research Laboratory (Department of the Environment)
Water Resources Board

M.R.C.

Department of Health and Social Security
Department of the Environment
Department of Trade and Industry
Foreign and Commonwealth Office—Overseas Development Administration
Home Office
Ministry of Agriculture, Fisheries and Food
Ministry of Defence
Post Office
Scottish Home and Health Department
United Kingdom Atomic Energy Authority

N.E.R.C.

Countryside Commission
Central Electricity Generating Board
Department of Agriculture and Fisheries, Scotland
Department of Health and Social Security
Department of the Environment
Department of Trade and Industry
Electricity Generating Boards
Forestry Commission
Highlands and Islands Development Board
Home Office
Local Authorities
Ministry of Agriculture Fisheries and Food
Ministry of Commerce, Northern Ireland
Ministry of Development, Northern Ireland
Ministry of Defence
National Coal Board
New Towns Development Corporations
Ordnance Survey
Port Authorities
Post Office
River Authorities
River Purification Boards
Scottish Development Department
United Kingdom Atomic Energy Authority
Water Resources Board

S.R.C.

British Broadcasting Corporation
Central Electricity Generating Board
Department of the Environment
Department of Trade and Industry
Independent Television Authority
Ministry of Aviation Supply
Ministry of Defence
Post Office
United Kingdom Atomic Energy Authority

In addition, all the Councils have many contacts with industrial firms and organisations.

C. THE WORK OF THE C.S.P.

17. Changes in Ministerial functions in 1964 resulted in the transfer of the responsibilities of the Minister for Science to the new Secretary of State for

Education and Science.[1] Following the recommendation of the Trend Committee (see paragraph 13(v) above), the Council for Scientific Policy was set up in January 1965 ' to advise the Secretary of State for Education and Science in the exercise of his responsibility for the formation and execution of Government science policy. '

18. The Council has 15 members drawn from universities, industry and research establishments; its meetings are attended by assessors from the 4 natural science Research Councils and the U.G.C. Because of the developing links between the C.S.P. and his Council, the Chairman of the S.S.R.C. has also attended the meetings of the C.S.P. for the last 2 years. C.S.P. papers have been circulated to other Government departments with an interest in its proceedings and some of these departments have sent assessors to its meetings.

19. Much of the C.S.P.'s work has been concerned with making the case for particular levels and growth rates for expenditure on science under the D.E.S. and with advising on the allocation of resources to the 4 Research Councils, the Royal Society, the Royal Society of Edinburgh, the Natural History Museum and the Office for Scientific and Technical Information. The total civil science budget on which the C.S.P. advises the Secretary of State is now nearly £120m. and in Table 2 below we show how this sum is distributed among the various agencies concerned. The way in which this total and its constituent parts have developed since 1965 is shown at Appendix A.

TABLE 2

SCIENCE VOTES ESTIMATES 1971–72

	(£ millions) Estimate	% of Total
A.R.C.	18·704	16·0
M.R.C.	23·015	19·6
N.E.R.C.	15·888	13·6
S.R.C.	55·733	47·5
Natural History Museum	1·877	1·6
Science: Grants and Services*	2·030	1·7
Total	117·247	100·0
S.S.R.C.†	4·141	—

* Including grants-in-aid to Royal Society and Royal Society of Edinburgh and the Office for Scientific and Technical Information (O.S.T.I.).
† The S.S.R.C. has come under the aegis of the C.S.P. in 1971.

20. The C.S.P. has concerned itself with other more general problems of scientific policy. Some of this work has been published (see Appendix B) and additional studies on the following subjects have recently been completed or are in progress:—

biological manpower, the proposed European laboratory for molecular biology, economic benefits of research, international scientific relations,

---

[1] A little later, in Autumn 1964, responsibility for the more applied and industrial work of the D.S.I.R. was transferred to the newly created Ministry of Technology (now D.T.I.) and other executive Government departments.

scientific interchange, survey of biological research, human resources in science and technology, implications for scientific research of university expansion, the determination of priorities in research and the support of scientific research in universities.

21. The function of the C.S.P. is purely advisory, and its advice is tendered to the Secretary of State for Education and Science, to whom the Research Councils also have direct access. This has meant that the C.S.P. has felt unable to concern itself too closely with the internal policies, priorities and organisation of individual Councils, although in the course of budgetary reviews it has tried to ensure that their major policies and new developments are generally serving national requirements. In particular, although it has noted and drawn attention to various problems—for instance, those of co-operation or overlap—the C.S.P. has not sought to intervene directly in any matter affecting the spread of scientific responsibility of an individual Research Council.

VI GENERAL DISCUSSION

A. BROAD CONSIDERATIONS

22. In our deliberations we have borne in mind some relevant features of the contemporary situation, to some of which reference has already been made and all of which we believe will increase rather than diminish in importance in the future.

23. The first point we have had to remember is the increasing pervasiveness of science and technology into all aspects of national activity, one result of which is the increasing need experienced by many executive organisations, including Government departments, to have ready access to tactical research to deal with specific problems. Additionally, at the level of basic research, it means that any given piece of basic research may have consequences for a large number of different sectors of national activity. The discovery of polythene, for example, was an unforeseen consequence of basic résearch in industry, springing from theories developed in universities concerning the effect of high pressures on chemical reactions, which in its turn, had even more diverse and unforeseen consequences; first, by facilitating the application of centimetric radar in wartime, and, at the other extreme, by enabling manufacturers to produce lighter and pleasanter domestic utensils. The fact that any piece of basic research finds many different users and not simply one is amply borne out by the study of the activities of the Research Councils, and is exemplified by the first Table in Chapter V.

24. Analyses of past technical achievements frequently show that they were based on many different pieces of basic research and the actual benefits of an individual basic research project have not lain in any one particular area of application. These factors make it extremely difficult in most cases to quantify the economic benefits of past research and almost impossible to use estimates of future economic gains from a projected basic research programme as a criterion for decision.

25. Another important point is that not only are the links between research and application complicated, but so also are the links between different pieces

9

of basic research. Although in certain phases of the history of science there has been great intellectual value, leading to rapid advances, in a fairly rigorous classification of science into different disciplines, the increasing importance of inter-disciplinary research, particularly exemplified in molecular biology, must be borne in mind in considering the organisation of research as a whole. But the importance of inter-disciplinary research, great though it is, is not the only manifestation of the inter-relatedness of different pieces of basic research. Advances in one discipline often lead indirectly, partly through improved instrumentation and other technological factors and partly through the introduction of new concepts, to advances in another.

26. A further point is the realisation that whereas the groupings, the conclusions, and the practical consequences of the sciences may change, the inherent characteristics of the scientific method remain constant, and it is therefore of fundamental importance for national scientific policy that there should be a corps of people soundly trained in the methods of scientific research.

27. These points: the pervasiveness of the consequences of science, the diversity of its users, the complexity of the connections between basic research and related economic benefits, the close relationships between different scientific disciplines, and the unifying importance of training in the methods of research, are, we believe, the most important general points about the nature of the scientific activity that we have to bear in mind in considering the Research Councils.

28. Additionally, we are faced with a series of problems that have become increasingly important matters of public concern.

29. Although we are convinced that science if adequately supported and properly managed will always be able to make a major contribution to the prosperity and wellbeing of society, we realise that there is now some public disillusion with science and concern with the adverse consequences of the use of at least some technologies, particularly in relation to the environment. Thus it may no longer be possible to assume that there will be general assent to the proposition that more science will make us wiser and richer. Nonetheless, it is certain that science must play a major role in the prevention of a further deterioration in our environment.

30. Because of the increasing pressure on government resources of other more directly appealing or social claims, we are now probably past the point of maximum growth rate of resources for science. This creates difficulties which are increased by ' sophistication ' (a term used to express the fact that it becomes more expensive to make equivalent advances in knowledge) and by the growth of ' big science ' (where the threshold of expenditure needed to achieve any worthwhile result tends to rise continually, as the fields of nuclear physics and radio-astronomy illustrate). This growth of expense for what might be considered the same ' amount ' of good science can partially be offset, for example, by increasing international collaboration and by selectivity in the support of science.

31. The consequence of an increasing need for selectivity in support of science and for an increasing amount of international science at a time of

decreasing popular approval of science will be that Research Councils will have to become increasingly well-informed about national needs and objectives, so that they may try to deploy scarce resources in the most appropriate direction, and be seen to be doing so. Though, as we have seen above, this is a task of considerable complexity, it is also one of immense importance and we regard it as imperative that those responsible for determining scientific priorities should be fully informed of and should pay due regard to government policy and national needs.

32. Finally, there is the growing realisation that we can no longer expect to improve existing technologies or introduce new developments by simple application of knowledge based on the physical and biological sciences. Increasingly we need to know more about ways in which such new knowledge can be used in harmony with the economic and human needs of the situation. And this calls for a much closer integration between the natural sciences and the social sciences, in research certainly, but also in the broader training of able people so that we may deploy our existing and new knowledge in ways which will give the maximum benefit to the community. Natural scientists will find it increasingly desirable to collaborate with social scientists in trying to determine the best objectives for and the probable consequences of their own activities. In some fields, notably the study of the control of environmental pollution, the development of social medicine and the encouragement of broader postgraduate training, joint work by the S.S.R.C. and other Research Councils is already going forward. We expect that there will be a growing range of activities in which such collaboration will be necessary.

B. THE RESEARCH COUNCIL PRINCIPLE

33. Basic and strategic science comprises an extremely complex network of scientific activities. Some of these can be classified into particular scientific disciplines but, as we have already mentioned, the boundaries between them are rapidly being eroded. We have been impressed by the great extent of multi- and inter-disciplinary work and by the rapidly increasing tendency for the interactions between the disciplines to grow stronger. The interactions are facilitated by having productive and imaginative scientists in day-to-day contact with colleagues working on related scientific projects with whom they can collaborate directly in new research. An interaction of this sort is quite unpredictable both in its nature and in the nature and extent of its consequences which may be the emergence of an entirely new area of scientific activity or the application of a particular scientific technique to an entirely different field of science. To maintain therefore strong and flexible linkages between scientists working in these fields it is important that they should be within the same organisation administered by people who recognise the benefit of these interactions and should not be dispersed to executive departments. For the same reason it is necessary to have a coherent policy for the whole of this scientific activity, especially during a period when costs are likely to grow more rapidly than resources.

34. Despite our belief that science is a unity and that it could only suffer by fragmentation corresponding to the responsibilities of different executive departments, we felt that we ought to analyse the activities of the Research

11

Councils with a view to seeing whether it would be practicable to assign these activities to particular individual users of research, since we recognise the need for close integration of the needs of users in the planning of research. Although at first sight the A.R.C., M.R.C. and N.E.R.C. might seem to fit naturally into M.A.F.F. (D.A.F.S.), D.H.S.S. (S.H.H.D.) and the Department of the Environment respectively, this analysis has convinced us that great difficulties would arise from a transfer of the activities even of these three Councils en bloc to different government departments; further, few if any of the Science Research Council and Social Science Research Council activities could be fitted appropriately into any executive Department of Government. The least difficulty would arise with the A.R.C. but even with this Council and more especially with the M.R.C. and N.E.R.C. the number of government departments and other organisations whose work is assisted by particular research programmes is surprisingly large (see Table 1 and Appendix C). For example, the applied psychology work which is undertaken by the M.R.C. is of very considerable value to the Post Office, to the Ministry of Defence, to D.T.I. and to Industry. To allocate an activity of this kind to a particular government department would create difficulties for the other interested government departments and would involve fragmentation of existing teams of scientists making their work much less effective than it otherwise would be. Moreover, if wasteful duplication is to be avoided and work in similar fields is to be properly co-ordinated, any such dispersal of activity even if it were feasible would necessitate the establishment of inter-connections between the separated parts which would be more numerous and more complex than the arrangements which now exist.

35. We have deliberately made no reference to the Haldane Report (Cd. 9230), traditionally regarded as the basis for the Research Council system, because we have examined the Research Council principle afresh in a modern context. For many years past it has been evident that Government departments need scientific knowledge (tactical science) and in some cases large scientific establishments to enable them to carry out their functions. But departments also need to be able to obtain help and independent advice from those who are engaged in strategic and basic science which underpins the work of several departments. It is essential that the advice and information from this source should be free from considerations of administrative and political convenience; but it does not mean that policies for strategic and basic science should be devised without proper regard for public policy. In fact, as we have argued above it is of paramount importance that public needs should be taken into consideration at all levels.

36. Despite the different ways in which the Councils operate, a large proportion of basic and strategic scientific activity is carried out within the universities where university and Research Council staff and funds are all involved with mutual benefit. This symbiotic relationship between the universities and the Research Councils is of the utmost importance. It provides the base from which future advances will be made and the education of future scientists beneficially influenced. To hope to replace this relationship by a whole series of relationships between the universities and a multiplicity of Government departments which in total would be equally beneficial is in our view unrealistic.

37. It is a characteristic of basic and strategic science that neither the devising of programmes of work nor the assignment of relative scientific priorities to each programme can be carried out by non-scientists. If wise decisions are to be made, programmes must be scrutinised and assessed by scientists of wide knowledge, much experience and a broad synoptic view of science. However, it is of the utmost importance that those making these judgments should be continually aware of national needs and objectives. Otherwise there will develop a dangerous and corrupting ' ivory towerism ', which will also impede the most effective transfer of scientific ideas and discoveries to practical use.

38. Finally, it is necessary to stress that the reduction of scientific co-ordination which would in our view be an inevitable consequence of the allocation of Research Councils to different executive bodies would result in a degree of financial inefficiency. Even with the addition of a complex of co-ordinating committees (themselves an extra cost) there would inevitably be an increased degree of overlapping and duplication within Government sponsored scientific research. We suggest that the nation cannot afford the loss of efficiency, scientific and financial, which this action would entail.

39. For all these reasons we recommend that whatever organisation is ultimately adopted to manage basic and strategic research it should be one that unifies rather than fragments scientific activity, one in which the determination of the scientific programmes is in the hands of scientists and one which retains a close association with the education and training of the scientists of the future. This is essentially a reaffirmation of the Research Council principle, to which we would add the essential qualification that the views and needs of departments, of industry and of professional users should be expressed at all levels, as much to those ' at the bench ' as to the policy makers.

C. THE NEED FOR CLOSER LINKS BETWEEN RESEARCH COUNCILS

40. In our view it is illogical on the one hand to assert the unity of science and the fluidity of its internal boundaries, and on the other hand to approve a system of completely independent Research Councils, each of which can only operate within relatively rigid boundaries set by its individual charter. The existence of these charters inevitably introduces a constraint which inhibits redeployment of effort and creates unnecessary demarcation problems. The Research Councils have recognised this; in the last few years some have reorganised their own internal boundaries and all have effected some co-ordination of their activities. Moreover, there are many matters of common concern which in varying degrees affect their policies and which they cannot determine alone. There is, for example, the major problem of the BALANCE OF EFFORT within disciplines such as biology which are supported by more than one Research Council and the timing and extent of any necessary redistribution of effort. There are also FIELDS, for example, pollution, where the five Research Councils have already collaborated on joint projects; such collaboration is likely to be needed more frequently in the future. Equally important is the question as to whether the BOUNDARIES have been correctly drawn, first, between responsibilities of individual Research Councils and, secondly, between them and the responsibilities for science of many

government departments. Growing international involvement in research will require increasingly close co-ordination of the Research Councils' policies. There are also questions of SCIENTIFIC MANPOWER that need study by educationalists and industrialists as well as by the Research Councils themselves: the number and kind of scientists required, balance between supply and demand, remedies for imbalance and the implications for the education of scientists. Finally, there are problems of STAFF POLICY: the desirability or otherwise of common grades and a common pension scheme and the promotion of mobility between the Research Councils and between them and industry, universities, and government departments.

41. We have already indicated that the Council for Scientific Policy has made studies of some of these problems as well as advising successive Secretaries of State about monetary allocations to the Research Councils both in the long-term and the short-term. It is, however, an advisory body only (see paragraph 21 above) and has no executive power to ensure that its recommendations are implemented. Its ability to determine policy has thus been limited to the influence which its discussions and published reports may have (an influence which is both varied and difficult to assess) and to the consequences for the Research Councils of its advice on financial allocations.

42. It could be argued that it would be possible to achieve much of the closer co-ordination and collaboration between Research Councils, which we see as likely to be of increasing importance in the future, within the present framework of separate chartered Research Councils; that a central body such as the C.S.P. could be strengthened and entrusted with responsibility for developments within the whole Research Council system.

43. Although we have given long and careful consideration to a possible strengthening of the C.S.P., we cannot see that this would be an effective solution even if on the advice of the Council, the Secretary of State were from time to time to use her power under the Science and Technology Act 1965 to direct the Research Councils on matters affecting the use and expenditure of public funds and their responsibility for particular activities. Such an arrangement would inevitably rely on convention only and the central body would lack the authority and power to translate its conclusions directly into actions, which we regard as essential if it is to be effective. It would still remain difficult to deal effectively with questions arising at the boundaries between Research Councils or between their activities and those of Government departments, to encourage scientific developments made necessary by the changing scientific scene and to determine priorities in a meaningful way across the whole Research Council field, having regard to major national needs.

VII PROPOSALS

44. For the reasons discussed above we conclude that our purpose could not be achieved by simple modification of the present system, and there must be some important changes. In particular it is essential that government departments should play their part in the formulation of scientific policy. The principles of scientific responsibility and of judgment on scientific merit which are the important characteristics of the Research Council system must, how-

ever, be preserved. To lose these would undermine the confidence which scientists justifiably have in the present system, which at the working level operates well and is highly regarded. In our view, this confidence would not survive the dismemberment of the Research Councils and the result would be a serious weakening of the national scientific effort.

45. Although our arguments would seem to point to the establishment of a monolithic National Research Council we are opposed to this solution. A single Council given authority and responsibility over the whole range of strategic and basic science might become too remote from the scientists actually carrying out the work; there would be a serious danger that a paralysing bureaucracy might develop. There would also be a risk that if the grant-giving authority were monolithic, its errors would have graver consequences.

46. The morale of the scientific community, and therefore its effectiveness in research or teaching, in large measure depends on the fact that the people who make the detailed decisions on scientific programmes, awards of grants, studentship policy etc., are known to and respected by the working scientist. It is vital to maintain this morale by retaining the degree of devolution of decision and discussion which at present exists and perhaps even to increase it. We conclude therefore that there should continue to be individual Research Councils, each with a scientist at its head, much as at present. Such Councils should be free to make and execute policy within areas which had been agreed by the mechanism described below; to formulate scientific policies related to objectives within their own fields; to make scientific assessments of projects and to commit funds for their support up to certain levels within their total budget and to manage their own staff. The present status of the chief officers of the Councils should also be preserved in order to retain the confidence of those with whom they have to negotiate. In this way we hope that the valuable and beneficial relationships which have been established between policy determining bodies such as the present Research Councils and their respective professional groups would be preserved and strengthened.

47. We recommend that the activities of the Research Councils should be co-ordinated and administered by a Board, which would include as full members the scientific heads of the Research Councils (at present either the Chairman or the Secretary). They have hitherto merely attended C.S.P. meetings as assessors. We regard it as essential that they should play a full part in the formulation and development of science policy, hearing and contributing to the arguments which apply in every field of science and sharing in corporate decision making.

48. Because of the very strong connection between scientific research and higher education, we believe that the Board should be associated with the Department of Education and Science. It would enjoy a relationship with the Department similar to that between the present Research Councils and the Department. It would be a statutory body with a charter which would protect the independence of Government-supported basic and strategic science and which would empower it to delegate authority to the Research Councils along the lines envisaged in paragraph 46 above.

15

49. The Board would be the main source of scientific advice to the Secretary of State for Education and Science and would make the case to her for the resources which it needed to carry out its tasks. Subject to the Secretary of State's power of direction it would determine broad problems of science policy (such as those mentioned in paragraph 40 above) including any necessary reorientation of that policy and any readjustment of the internal boundaries between Research Councils, and would allocate resources to the individual Research Councils. It would also be able to add to and subtract from the number of the Research Councils, in response, for example, to the growth of new disciplines and the emergence of new professional groups. It should not however at any stage so reduce the number of Research Councils that the virtues of the specialist Council were lost.

50. In addition to the scientific heads of the Research Councils, the Board should include a substantial number of independent members; some of these would be professional scientists whose combined knowledge would broadly cover the range of the natural and social sciences embraced by the Research Councils, and some would be persons with an understanding and experience of science-in-action, most of them drawn from public or private industry. The Royal Society occupies a special position in the scientific life of the country and for this reason we believe that the President should always be a member. Since more than half the students in universities are in science-based faculties, one member should be a Vice-Chancellor. The Chairman of the U.G.C. should also be a member.

51. In order that the Board may be fully and continually aware of public policy and of those needs of executive departments of Government which can be served by the scientific activities of Research Councils and in order that wasteful overlap or duplication may be avoided, it is essential that Government departments should be informed about the Board's activities and that they should be guaranteed access to the Board's discussions and should be able to raise at Board level matters of interest to them, which had a bearing on Research Council activities. The Board should therefore include, as members, playing a full part in decision-making, representatives from Government departments with major scientific interests. We suggest that the Chief Scientific Adviser, Cabinet Office and an appropriate officer of the D.E.S. should be two such members and that, so as not to make the Board too big, three other members should be appointed, perhaps in rotation, from other departments closely concerned with the Board's work. Other departments should receive the Board's papers and be able to attend any meeting discussing matters of direct interest to them. The Board should also from time to time arrange special discussions on policies and programmes to which appropriate user interests, both inside and outside government, should be invited. We would, however, wish to emphasise very strongly that the views of Government departments should not be expressed at Board level only but should continue to be heard and to exert influence at the level of the Research Councils and at any other lower level which is thought to be appropriate and necessary. Conversely, we see comparable advantages in representation of the Research Council system on advisory bodies of other government departments.

52. The organisational arrangement we envisage for the proposed Board is shown in the following diagram:

SECRETARY OF STATE

BOARD OF THE RESEARCH COUNCILS

Chairman (Accounting Officer)

Independent Members

President of the Royal Society, Vice-Chancellor 1, DES 1,
Cabinet Office1, Other Ministries 3, UGC1.

Scientific Heads of Research Councils

RESEARCH COUNCILS

53. The task of the Chairman would be a highly responsible one: his duties would be onerous and could not be discharged on a part-time basis. We, therefore, propose that he should be appointed full-time for a prescribed period with very limited possibility of renewal of the appointment only in exceptional cases. It is clearly highly desirable that most of his working life should have been spent as a scientist rather than an administrator. He would be the Research Councils' natural link with the rest of the Government's effort in research and development, and should represent the Research Council system on any central body concerned with the co-ordination of the Government's overall R. & D. programme. One of the independent members should be appointed Deputy Chairman to help him in these responsible tasks, and the Board would certainly require its own secretariat.

54. The Research Council and independent members of the Board would be appointed by the Secretary of State for Education and Science. In order to preserve the status of the individual Councils, we would like their Chairmen and members to be appointed by the Secretary of State after consultation with the Board, with her ministerial colleagues where appropriate, and in the case of scientific members, with the P.R.S. Existing arrangements for the appointment of representatives from other departments would remain unaffected. The full-time chief officer of each Council (where not himself the Chairman) should also be appointed by the Secretary of State on the advice of the Board and the P.R.S. In practice one would expect that conventions would develop which would simplify the consultational processes.

55. Before the Board is established, careful consideration should be given to the scope and extent of its responsibilities. Our analysis of the work of the Research Councils has convinced us that, whilst most of the work of all the existing Research Councils would fall naturally within its competence, there are certain areas of activity within the present Research Council structure which merit further study to see whether they ought not to be transferred to some other department of Government and equally there are activities at present within the responsibility of departments of Government which might after examination be better placed within the jurisdiction of the Board. In particular, we think it would be inappropriate for the Board to assume financial responsibility for independent private bodies such as the Royal Society or for institutions such as the Natural History Museum. In our view under the new arrangements these might receive their financial support direct from the D.E.S. We have had neither time nor opportunity to examine specific areas where transfer into or out of the Research Council system might be advisable. The main point we wish to make here is that there is a whole range of such problems needing detailed study in which the C.S.P. or, after its establishment, the Board should participate.

56. The acceptance of these proposals would mean the dissolution of the C.S.P. and devolution of some of the responsibilities of the Department of Education and Science. In particular, it would be logical if some of the functions and responsibilites now discharged by the Science Branch of the D.E.S., including international scientific relations, were to be transferred to the Board.

VIII   SUMMARY OF CONCLUSIONS AND PROPOSALS

57.

(i) The Research Council structure with its specialist control of a wide range of highly sophisticated activities appears essential for the best administration and conduct of this area of government-sponsored scientific activity in the U.K. which we consider to be of great importance. It has however certain disadvantages arising from a limited ability of adjustment to changing circumstances, and requires modification (paragraphs 40, 44–46).

(ii) The network of responsibilities and inter-relationships of the Research Councils, is however of such a nature that they could not each be assigned to one uniquely appropriate department. Were each to be administered by an executive department, new and complicated co-ordinating committee structures would be necessary, which would lead to overall loss of efficiency scientifically, administratively and financially (paragraph 34).

(iii) In order to retain the advantages of the Research Council system, while providing for stronger links with the needs and policies of government departments and for the possibility of adjustments of responsibilities between Councils and the transfer of specific activities both into and out of their field, we propose the replacement of the Council for Scientific Policy by a new chartered body, here referred to as the Board of the Research Councils, responsible to the Secretary of State for Education and Science (paragraph 47).

(iv) This Board would consist of a Chairman, the scientific heads of the Research Councils, the President of the Royal Society, a university Vice-Chancellor, independent members, members from the most relevant Government organisations and from the U.G.C. and assessors from other Government departments. Under the Secretary of State it would be responsible for financial allocations to the individual Councils, and would keep under review their broad policies and their range of responsibilities with the power to make necessary modifications, although each Council would be free to make and execute policies within its area of responsibility (paragraphs 46–51).

(v) The Board would have the overall responsibility of ensuring that the requirements of executive departments for scientific support from Research Councils were being properly met, on a service or contract basis where appropriate, and by the provision of independent and authoritative information and advice in other cases (paragraph 51).

(vi) We believe that these proposals represent a natural evolution from the present system and that they would combine the very considerable advantages that this system has for individual scientists, for scientific organisations and for the universities with greater flexibility and an improved capacity for service to Government departments and to the community.

APPENDIX A

THE GROWTH AND DISTRIBUTION OF SCIENCE VOTES
(ESTIMATES, EXCLUDING SUPPLEMENTARIES)

	1965-66		1966-67			1967-68			1968-69			1969-70			1970-71			1971-72		
	£m. Estimate	% of Total	£m. Estimate	% of Total	% Growth	£m. Estimate	% of Total	% Growth	£m. Estimate	% of Total	% Growth	£m. Estimate	% of Total	% Growth	£m. Estimate	% of Total	% Growth	£m. Estimate	% of Total	% Growth
A.R.C. …	9·313	17·4	10·312	16·3	7·3	11·974	16·5	12·2	13·172	16·1	7·3	14·663	15·9	3·2	16·208	15·7	7·0	18·704	16·0	3·1
M.R.C. …	10·279	19·2	11·885	18·7	11·6	14·232	19·6	14·9	15·339	18·7	5·1	17·141	18·6	6·9	19·670	19·1	8·1	23·015	19·6	3·6
N.E.R.C. …	4·021	7·5	5·376	8·5	17·8	7·657	10·5	20·6	8·994	11·0	13·5	11·725	12·7	20·4	13·919	13·5	10·4	15·888	13·6	5·3
S.R.C. …	28·476	53·2	33·919	53·6	13·2	36·584	50·4	6·9	41·916	51·1	5·4	45·844	49·7	2·9	49·612	48·0	3·8	55·733	47·5	4·8
N.H.M. …	0·884	1·6	0·931	1·5	1·3	0·957	1·3	—	(a)1·031	1·2	6·0	(a)1·239	1·3	9·7	(a)1·841	1·8	41·4	(a)1·877	1·6	-9·8
S.:G. & S.*	0·598	1·1	0·878	1·4	41·2	(b)1·203	1·7	30·5	(b)1·568	1·9	24·6	(b)1·710	1·8	3·8	(b)1·997	1·9	10·2	2·030	1·7	16·8
Total …	53·571	100·0	63·301	100·0	12·2	72·607	100·0	10·8	82·020	100·0	6·8	92·322	100·0	5·7	103·227	100·0	6·5	117·247	100·0	4·3
S.S.R.C. …	0·028	—	0·772	—	—	1·162	—	47·3	1·728	—	47·9	2·380	—	25·9	3·264	—	30·3	4·141	—	16·0

The percentage growth figures for separate Votes and for the overall total, are calculated in *real* terms and for equivalent responsibilities in consecutive years.

* Includes grant-in-aid to Royal Society, Royal Society, Edinburgh and Office for Scientific and Technical Information (O.S.T.I.).
(a) Includes costs of new buildings borne on D.O.E. (M.P.B.W. before 1971/72) Vote (1968-69 = £0·020m, 1969-70 = £0·135m, 1971-71 = £0·596m, 1971-72 = £0·453m).
(b) Includes costs of Documentation Processing Centre borne on D.E.S., M.P.B.W., H.M.S.O. Votes (1967-68 = £0·150m, 1968-69 = £0·214m, 1969-70 = £0·255m, 1970-71 = £0·383m).

C.S.P. PUBLICATIONS

1. A Report of a Joint Working Group on Computers for Research
   (Chairman: Professor B. H. Flowers)
   Cmnd. 2883, Price 32½p, Date January 1966

2. Interim Report—Enquiry into the Flow of Candidates in Science and Technology into Higher Education
   (Chairman: Dr. F. S. Dainton)
   Cmnd. 2893, Price 15p, Date February 1966 (out-of-print)

3. Report on Science Policy
   Cmnd. 3007, Price 15p, Date May 1966

4. Report of the Working Party on Liaison Between Universities and Government Research Establishments
   (Chairman: Sir Gordon Sutherland)
   Cmnd. 3222, Price 72½p, Date March 1967

5. Second Report on Science Policy
   Cmnd. 3420, Price 21p, Date October 1967

6. The Proposed 300 GeV Accelerator
   (Chairman: Professor M. M. Swann)
   Cmnd. 3503, Price 39p, Date January 1968

7. Enquiry into the Flow of candidates in Science and Technology into Higher Education
   (Chairman: Dr. F. S. Dainton)
   Cmnd. 3541, Price 72½p, Date February 1968

8. Report of the Working Group on Molecular Biology
   (Chairman: Dr. J. C. Kendrew)
   Cmnd. 3675, Price 12½p, Date July 1968

9.*The Flow into Employment of Scientists, Engineers and Technologists
   (Chairman: Professor Michael Swann)
   Cmnd. 3760, Price 87½p, Date September 1968

SCIENCE POLICY STUDIES

No 1. The Sophistication Factor in Science Expenditure
   (Authors: A. V. Cohen and L. N. Ivins)
   SO Code No. 27-418-1, Price 30p, Date 1967

No 2. Occupational Choice
   (Author: J. A. Butler, M.A.)
   SO Code No. 27-418-2, Price 17½p, Date 1968

No 3. The Employment of Highly Specialised Graduates
   (Author: M. C. McCarthy)
   SO Code No. 27-418-3, Price 22½p, Date 1968

No 4. An Attempt to Quantify the Economic Benefits of Scientific Research
   (Authors: I. C. R. Byatt and A. V. Cohen)
   SBN 11 270139 6, Price 20p, Date October 1969

---

* jointly with the Committee on Manpower Resources (C.M.R.)

RESEARCH COUNCIL PROGRAMME ANALYSES

KEY TO ABBREVIATIONS

A.R.C.	Agricultural Research Council
B.B.C.	British Broadcasting Corporation
B.E.A.M.A.	British Electrical and Allied Manufacturers' Association
B.R.S.	Building Research Station
C.A.B.	Commonwealth Agricultural Bureaux
C.A.s	Crown Agents
C.B.S.	Cattle Breeding Station
C.C.	Countryside Commission
C.E.G.B.	Central Electricity Generating Board
C.V.L.	Central Veterinary Laboratory
D.A.F.S.	Department of Agriculture and Fisheries, Scotland
D.O.E.	Department of the Environment
D.T.I.	Department of Trade and Industry
E.G.B.s	Electricity Generating Boards
F.A.O.	Food and Agriculture Organisation (United Nations)
F.C.	Forestry Commission
F.C.O.	Foreign and Commonwealth Office
H.G.C.A.	Home Grown Cereals Authority
H.I.D.B.	Highlands and Islands Development Board
H.M.B.	Hop Marketing Board
H.O.	Home Office
I.T.A.	Independent Television Authority
L.A.s	Local Authorities
L.H.A.s	Lighthouse Authorities
M.A.F.F.	Ministry of Agriculture, Fisheries and Food
M.A.S.	Ministry of Aviation Supply
M.C.N.I.	Ministry of Commerce (Northern Ireland)
M.D.N.I.	Ministry of Development (Northern Ireland)
M.L.C.	Meat and Livestock Commission
M.M.B.	Milk Marketing Board
M.o.D.(N)	Ministry of Defence (Navy)
M.R.C.	Medical Research Council
M.R.C.C.	Mineral Resources Consultative Committee
N.C.B.	National Coal Board
N.E.R.C.	Natural Environment Research Council
N.I.A.B.	National Institute of Agricultural Botany
N.S.A.	Nuclear Stock Association
N.T.D.C.	New Towns Development Corporation
O.D.A.	Overseas Development Administration (F.C.O.)
O.E.C.D.	Organisation for Economic Co-operation and Development
O.S.	Ordnance Survey
P.A.s	Port Authorities
P.G.R.O.	Pea Growing Research Organisation
P.H.L.S.	Public Health Laboratory Service
P.M.B.	Potato Marketing Board
P.O.	Post Office
P.P.L.	Plant Pathology Laboratory
R.A.s	Research Associations
Riv. As.	River Authorities
R.P.B.s	River Purification Boards
R.R.L.	Road Research Laboratory

S.B.R.E.C.	Sugar Beet Research and Education Committee
S.D.D.	Scottish Development Department
S.H.D.	Scottish Health Department
S.R.C.	Science Research Council
S.S.R.C.	Social Science Research Council
U.K.A.E.A.	United Kingdom Atomic Energy Authority
U.K.C.C.F.S.T.	U.K. Co-ordinating Committee for Food Science and Technology
V.I.S.	Veterinary Investigation Service
W.B.s	Water Boards
W.F.A.	White Fish Authority
W.H.O.	World Health Organisation (United Nations)
W.P.R.L.	Water Pollution Research Laboratory
W.R.B.	Water Resources Board

TABLE 1
A.R.C. PROGRAMME ANALYSIS
(1970–71 Estimates, including supplementaries)

£'000

Primary Field of Investigation	Links with Other Primary Fields	Links with Work of Other Bodies	Sector of Expenditure					Totals	
			A.R.C. Institutes (1)	Research Units* (2)	State-aided Institutes			excl. (4) (5)	incl. (4) (6)
					A.R.C. (3)	D.A.F.S. (4)			
A. Soils									
A1. Structure and composition	A2–4; B3–8; F1–2	R.R.L., B.R.S., N.E.R.C.	51	29	344	462		424	886
A2. Drainage and irrigation	A1, 3–4; B3–8; F1–2	W.P.R.L. (D.O.E.) W.R.B., Riv.As.	—	—	43·5	—		43·5	43·5
A3. Tillage	A1–2, 4; B3–8; F1–2		—	14	—	—		14	14
A4. Fertility	A1–3; B3–8; F1–2	F.C., N.E.R.C., Fertiliser and pesticide industry.	23·5	190·5	235·5	180		451·5	631·5
A. TOTAL ...			76·5	233·5	623	642		933	1,575
B. Plants									
B1. Breeding ...	B2, 3–7; E2; F1–3; G	N.I.A.B., Food R.A.s, P.M.B., H.M.B., H.G.C.A. Eucarpia† N.S.A., Commercial plant-breeders and seedsmen.	—	18	1,279·5	399		1,297·5	1,696·5

* including research grants and special equipment grants.
† European association of plant breeders

24

	Codes	Organisations						£'000
B2. Plant protection	A4; B1, 3–8; E2; F1–2	F.A.O., O.E.C.D., N.E.R.C., P.P.L. (M.A.F.F.), Commonwealth agricultural institutions, commercial and industrial organisations.	195·5	402·5	1,779·5	187·5	2,377·5	2,565
B3–8 Plant husbandry	A1–4; B1–2; E2; F1–3	F.A.O., O.E.C.D., P.M.B., H.G.C.A., S.B.R.E.C., fertilizer and agro-chemical industries, agricultural machine industries, growers' associations.	192·5	323	2,265·5	239	2,781	3,020
B3. Grassland B4. Field crops B5. Perennial crops B6. Vegetable B7. Protected crops (including mushrooms) B8. Ornamental								
B. TOTAL			388	743·5	5,324·5	825·5	6,456	7,281
C. Poultry								
C1. Breeding*			—	0·5	—	—	0·5	0·5
C2. Disease ...	C3; E1	P.H.L.S. F.A.O., W.H.O., M.A.F.F. veterinary laboratory and investigation services, pharmaceutical firms.	25	20	587·5	—	632·5	632·5
C3. Husbandry ...	C2; E1; F1		731	30	67·5	—	828·5	828·5
C. TOTAL			756	50·5	655·0	—	1,461·5	1,461·5

25

TABLE 1—continued

£'000

| Primary Field of Investigation | Links with Other Primary Fields | Links with Work of Other Bodies | Sector of Expenditure | | | | | |
			A.R.C. Institutes (1)	Research Units* (2)	State-aided Institutes A.R.C. (3)	State-aided Institutes D.A.F.S. (4)	Totals excl. (4) (5)	Totals incl. (4) (6)
D. Animals other than Poultry								
D1. Breeding	D2–3; E1	M.M.B., M.L.C., C.A.B., Cattle Breeding Centre (M.A.F.F.), commercial breeding companies.	415·5	132	—	—	547·5	547·5
D2. Disease	D1, 3; E1	C.V.L. (M.A.F.F.), V.I.S. (M.A.F.F.), F.A.O., W.H.O., M.M.B., M.L.C., P.H.L.S., veterinary schools, pharmaceutical firms.	1,005	87·5	873	499	1,965·5	2,464·5
D3. Husbandry	D1–2; E1; F1	M.M.B., M.L.C., H.G.C.A., P.H.L.S., Food R.A.s, F.A.O.	972·5	397·5	1,053·5	1,175	2,423·5	3,598·5
D. TOTAL			2,393	617	1,926·5	1,674	4,936·5	6,610·5

	Code	Collaborating bodies						
E. Food								
E1. Animal production	C1–3; D1–3; F1, 3	Food R.A.s, M.R.C., U.K.C.C.F.S.T., P.H.L.S., commercial firms.	394	11	232·5	89·5	882·5	972
E2. Plant production	B1–2, 4–8; F1–2	Food R.A.s, M.R.C., P.G.R.O., P.M.B., H.G.C.A., S.B.R.E.C., H.M.B.	361	6	239·5	—	606·5	606·5
E. TOTAL ...			755	17	472	89·5	1,489	1,578·5
F. Buildings, machinery and equipment								
F1. Farming ...	A3–4; B2–6; C3; D3; E1–2	B.R.S., W.P.R.L., National Agricultural College of Royal Agricultural Society of England, engineering industry.	—	4·5	816	254	820·5	1,074·5
F2. Horticultural ...	A3–4; B2, 6–8; E2	B.E.A.M.A., B.R.S., engineering industry.	—	—	266·5	—	266·5	266·5
F3. Food processing (including dairying)	D3; E1	M.M.B., engineering industry.	—	—	45	—	45	45
F. TOTAL ...			—	4·5	1,127·5	254	1,132	1,386

27

Table 1—continued

£'000

Primary Field of Investigation	Links with Other Primary Fields	Links with Work of Other Bodies	Sector of Expenditure				Totals	
			A.R.C. Institutes (1)	Research Units* (2)	State-aided Institutes		excl. (4) (5)	incl. (4) (6)
					A.R.C. (3)	D.A.F.S. (4)		
G. Other								
Bees ...	B2, 3–8		—	—	52	—	52	52
A–G. TOTAL ...			4,368·5	1,666	10,180·5	3,485	16,215	19,700
A–G. RECEIPTS ...								75
A–G. TOTAL (net) ...								19,625
A.R.C. H.Q. and other costs ...								627
TOTAL net expenditure ...								20,252

28

TABLE 2
M.R.C. PROGRAMME ANALYSIS
(1968–69 out-turn)

£'000

Primary Fields of Investigation	Links with Other Primary Fields	Links with Other Bodies	Sector of Expenditure				Totals
			M.R.C. Research Units	National Institute for Medical Research and Clinical Research Centre	Grant-aided Institutions	M.R.C. Research Groups and Grants	
A General Clinical							
A1 General Clinical Medicine (including Clinical Research Centre) … … …	Too many to list	Health Depts.	42	509	—	—	551
A2 Obstetrics and gynaecology …	A11, B1, A14, A6, C1, C2, C3, C4, E4, E3, F3	A.R.C.	53	—	—	76	129
A3 Dermatology … …	C1, C2, A14, C3, E2, F3, A12,	Health	42	—	—	25	67
A4 Cardiovascular Disease	E4, C4	Health	141	18	—	95	254
A5 Respiratory Disorders …	D1, A4, B1	Health	—	—	—	70	70
A6 Renal Disorders … …	A4, C1, A14	Health	6	—	—	27	33
A7 Gastroenterology … …	C1, C2, C4	Health	43	—	—	125	168
A8 Locomotor Disorders …	C1, C2, E4	Health	259	—	—	27	286
A9 Metabolic Disorders …	E4, A14, F1	Health	96	—	—	65	161
A10 Clinical Bioengineering …	A7, A1, A8, A4, etc.	S.R.C.	63	46	—	17	126
A11 Clinical Physiology … …	Too many to list	Health	15	—	—	46	61
A12 Clinical Pharmacology …	Too many to list	Health	—	—	—	40	40
A13 Clinical Pathology … …	Too many to list	Health	—	—	—	16	16
A14 Clinical Biochemistry …	Too many to list	Health	9	—	—	34	43
A. TOTAL … … …			769	573	—	663	2,005

29

TABLE 2—*continued*

£'000

Primary Fields of Investigation	Links with Other Primary Fields	Links with Other Bodies	Sector of Expenditure				Totals
			M.R.C. Research Units	National Institute for Medical Research and Clinical Research Centre	Grant-aided Institutions	M.R.C. Research Groups and Grants	
B *Cellular Disorders Section*							
B1 Cancer	B2, B3, B5, B6, B7, C1, C2, C3, D1, D2, E2, E3, E4, F3, etc.	Health Depts.	264	36	612	71	983
B2 Radiation... ...	B1, D1	A.R.C., A.E.A Health	1,083	—	—	93	1,176
B3 Developmental Biology	B1, B5, B4, B6	A.R.C., S.R.C.	22	100	—	33	155
B4 Ageing	B3, B6		—	—	—	14	14
B5 Genetics	Too many to list	S.R.C., A.R.C.	446	36	—	72	554
B6 Molecular Biology ...	B1, B3, B5, C1, C2, C3, etc.	S.R.C.	459	92	—	316	867
B7 Related Biochemistry ...	Too many to list	S.R.C.	103	178	—	9	290
B8 Other Projects			92	—	24	83	199
B TOTAL			2,469	442	651	691	4,238

30

								£'000
C	*Infectious and Immune Diseases*							
C1	Immunology and applications	Too many to list	A.R.C., Health Depts.	79	197	27	235	538
C2	Microbiology and infections	Too many to list	S.R.C., A.R.C. Health M.A.F.F	246	280	35	206	767
C3	Blood Diseases	B1, B2, B5, B6, C2, A4, E4	A.R.C. Health	204	—	148	123	475
C4	Nutrition	G3, A7, A14, B7, A4, etc.	A.R.C. Health M.A.F.F.	168	—	—	42	210
C5	Dental Research	C2, C4	Health	36	—	—	21	57
C6	Laboratory Animals	Too many to list	A.R.C.	172	—	—	—	172
C	TOTAL			905	477	210	627	2,219
D.	*Environmental Industrial Medicine*							
D1.	Occupational health and toxicology	B1, B2, F1, F2, E2, E3, C2, A1, A5, D2, D3	D.O.E., D.T.I., N.E.R.C., A.R.C., M.A.F.F., etc.	580	—	—	42	622
D2.	Pharmacology	D1, A12, B6, B7,		57	213	—	—	270
D3.	Job efficiency:							
	(a) Applied physiology	A3, A4, A5, A10 D1, etc.	D.T.I., H.O., Post Office, M.O.D., M.A.F.F., S.S.R.C., S.R.C.	56	224	—	1	281
	(b) Applied psychology	F1, F2, D1		228	—	—	50	278
D.	TOTAL			921	437	—	93	1,451

TABLE 2—continued

£'000

Primary Fields of Investigation	Links with Other Primary Fields	Links with Other Bodies	Sector of Expenditure				TOTALS
			M.R.C. Research Units	National Institute for Medical Research and Clinical Research Centre	Grant-aided Institutions	M.R.C. Research Groups and Grants	
E. Social Medicine							
E1. Computer science ...	Too many to list	All Councils	170	—	—	144	314
E2. Epidemiology: Medical statistics	Too many to list	S.S.R.C. Health Depts.	76	—	—	5	81
E3. Social and preventive medicine: medical sociology	Too many to list	S.S.R.C., Health H.O.	127	—	—	15	142
E4. Human genetics ...	Too many to list	S.S.R.C., Health	148	—	—	9	157
E. TOTAL			521	—	—	173	694
F. Nervous Disorders							
F1. Psychiatry and psychology	F2, F3, A12, E3, E4, D3, A1	S.S.R.C., Health Depts.	433	—	—	160	593

							£'000
F2. Neurology, neuro-physiology, special senses	F1, F3, F4, Most of A, D2, E4	S.R.C., Health	202	92	—	455	749
F3. Endocrinology	F2, A2, A4, A5, B1	Health	213	36	6	194	449
F4. Anaesthesia	A12, F2	Health	—	—	—	28	28
F. TOTAL			848	128	6	837	1,819
G. Tropical Medicine Section							
G1. Infectious diseases (a) Bacteria and viruses (b) Protozoa and helminths	C2, B1, E12, G4, G2 / C1, C2, C3, G4, G2	M.o.D., O.D.A. / O.D.A.	85 / 182	36 / 141	— / —	17 / 80	138 / 403
G2. Epidemiology ...	G1, G2, V1, A4, etc.	O.D.A.	47	—	—	6	53
G3. Nutrition	C4, G1	O.D.A.	164	—	—	5	169
G4. Other research grants			—	—	—	9	9
G. TOTAL			478	177	—	117	772
A–G. TOTAL			6,911	2,234	852*	3,201	13,198
Capital Expenditure ... Training Awards ... ... H.Q. and Central Expenses							1,897 / 742 / 823
TOTAL (gross) expenditure							16,660

* includes international subscription to I.A.R.C.

33

TABLE 3

N.E.R.C. PROGRAMME ANALYSIS
(1970–71 Estimates)

£'000

Primary Field of Investigation	Links with Other Primary Fields	Links with Work of Other Bodies (i) Research Functions (ii) Other Functions	Sector of Expenditure				
			Component Bodies and Research Units	Grant-aided Associations	University Grants	University Training	Total
			(1)	(2)	(3)	(4)	(5)
A. The Earth A1. Structure and composition of U.K. land mass.	A2–5, 8	(i) A.R.C., M.A.F.F., N.C.B. (ii) D.O.E., M.A.F.F., M.C.N.I. N.C.B., N.T.D.C., L.A.s	1,037	—	244	65	1,346
A2. Structure and composition of U.K. continental shelf	A1, 3, 7	(i) M.o.D., D.O.E. (ii) D.T.I., D.O.E., M.o.D., P.O.	1,092	—	45	58	1,195
A3. Mineral resources (U.K. land, continental shelf and overseas)	A1–2, 7, 8	(i) D.T.I., U.K.A.E.A., N.C.B. (ii) F.C.O., D.O.E., D.T.I., U.K.A.E.A., N.C.B., M.R.C.C.	1,047	—	47	56	1,150
A4. Physical properties of rocks and soils	A1, 5	(i) D.O.E., N.C.B., (ii) D.O.E., M.A.F.F., F.C.O., N.C.B., N.T.D.C., L.A.s, Riv.A.s, W.B.s	157	—	49	11	217
A5. Underground water... ...	A1, 4; C1	(i) W.R.B., Riv.A.s (ii) F.C.O., W.R.B., L.A.s, Riv.A.s, W.B.s	303	—	9	16	328
A6. General structure and properties of the earth's interior and continental crust and mantle	A7, 8	(i) S.R.C., U.K.A.E.A. (ii) F.C.O., U.K.A.E.A.	962	—	205	60	1,227

							£'000
A7. Structure and composition of the oceanic crust and mantle	A2–3, 6, 8	(i) M.o.D, U.K.A.E.A. (ii) F.C.O., D.T.I, M.o.D, U.K.A.E.A., P.O.	195	—	205	60	1,227
A8. Earth's magnetism ...	A1, 3, 6–7; E2	(i) S.R.C., M.o.D, P.O. (ii) M.o.D, U.K.A.E.A, P.O.	206	—	59	14	279
A9. Glaciology	E4	(i) S.R.C. (ii) M.o.D.	105	—	12	6	123
A. TOTAL			5,104	—	711	298	6,113
B. Oceans and Seas B1. Currents and circulation of oceans and seas	B2–4, 6–9	(i) S.R.C., M.A.F.F./D.A.F.S., D.O.E., M.o.D, (N) (ii) M.A.F.F./D.A.F.s, D.T.I., D.O.E. M.o.D., U.K.A.E.A., L.A.s	409	334	46	25	514
B2. Physical and chemical properties of water masses	B1, 3–4, 7–8	(i) S.R.C., M.A.F.F./D.A.F.S. D.O.E., M.o.D.(N) (ii) M.A.F.F./D.A.F.S, D.T.I., D.O.E., M.o.D, U.K.A.E.A., L.A.s, W.R.B.	97	41	10	7	155
B3. Interaction between ocean and atmosphere	B1–2, 4, 7–8; E1, 4	(i) M.A.F.F./D.A.F.S, D.O.E. M.o.D. (ii) M.o.D, D.T.I., D.O.E, M.A.F.F/D.A.F.S, S.D.D., L.A.s, CA.s, P.A.s, L.H.A.s, E.G.B.s	133	—	23	8	164
B4. Tides	B1–3, 7–8	(i) M.o.D, D.O.E. (ii) M.o.D., M.A.F.F, D.T.I., D.O.E, O.S., L.A.s, P.A.s	310	6	—	16	332

TABLE 3—continued

£'000

Primary Field of Investigation	Links with Other Primary Fields	Links with Work of Other Bodies (i) Research Functions (ii) Other Functions	Sector of expenditure				
			Component Bodies and Research Units	Grant-aided Associations	University Grants	University Training	Total
B5. Biology and ecology of marine organisms and communities	B1–2, 6–9	(i) S.R.C., M.A.F.F./D.A.FS. (ii) M.A.F.F./D.A.F.S., D.T.I., H.O.	743	360	48	59	1,210
B6. Biological resources of the sea	B1–2, 5, 8–9	(i) M.A.F.F/D.A.FS., W.F.A. (ii) M.A.F.F/D.A.F.S., W.F.A., H.I.D.B., C.E.G.B.	56	237	19	16	328
B7. Properties and movements of the seabed surface	A2, 4; B1–4, 8	(i) M.o.D., D.O.E. (ii) M.o.D., D.T.I., D.O.E., M.A.F.F/D.A.F.S., L.A.s, P.A.s	239	13	—	13	265
B8. Special problems of coasts and estuaries	B2, 4–7, 9; C2–3; D3	(i) S.R.C., D.O.E., M.A.F.F., P.A.s, E.G.B.s (ii) D.O.E., M.A.F.F., L.A.s, P.A.s, W.R.B., E.G.B.s	66	83	22	9	180
B9. Marine pollution ...	B1–8; E4	(i) M.R.C., S.R.C., S.S.R.C., D.O.E. (ii) D.T.I., D.O.E., M.A.F.F/ D.A.F.S., D.H.S.S., L.A.s, C.E.G.B.	3	35	37	4	79
B. TOTAL...			2,056	809	205	157	3,227

							£'000
C. Inland Waters							
C1. Water balance of catchments	A4–5; C2; D4; E.1,3	(i) A.R.C., Mod, D.O.E., W.R.B., Riv.As, (ii) D.O.E., D.T.I., M.A.F.F., F.C.O., M.o.D., W.R.B., Riv.As, R.P.B.s, W.B.s, L.A.s	314	—	30	18	362
C2. River regimes ...	A4–5; B4, 8; C3; E3	(i) Mod., D.O.E., W.R.B., Riv.As (ii) D.O.E., M.A.F.F., M.o.D., M.D.N.I., W.R.B., Riv.As, R.P.B.s, W.B.s, L.A.s	156	—	6	8	170
C3. Biology and ecology of freshwater organisms and communities	C2, 4–5	(i) A.R.C., S.R.C., M.A.F.F./D.A.F.S., D.O.E. (ii) M.A.F.F./D.A.F.S., D.O.E., W.R.B., Riv.As, W.B.s	46	266	26	17	355
C4. Biological resources of inland waters	C2–3, 5	(i) A.R.C., M.A.F.F./D.A.F.S. (ii) M.A.F.F./D.A.F.S., D.O.E., W.R.B., Riv.As, W.B.s	—	76	18	5	99
C5. Pollution of inland waters ...	C3–4; D4	(i) M.A.F.F./D.A.F.S., D.O.E. (ii) M.A.F.F./D.A.F.S., D.O.E., W.R.B. Riv.As, W.B.s	15	15	23	3	56
C. Total			531	357	103	51	1,042
D. Countryside							
D1. Ecology of natural habitats and biology of wildlife	B8; C3; D2–3	(i) A.R.C., S.R.C. (ii) D.O.E. N. Ireland Govt., L.A.s	836	21	114	49	1,020
D2. Biological resources of the countryside (except agriculture)	D1, 3	(i) S.S.R.C., F.C. (ii) F.C.O, C.C., L.A.s	171	14	96	14	295

37

TABLE 3—continued

£'000

Primary Field of Investigation	Links with Other Primary Fields	Links with Work of Other Bodies (i) Research Functions (ii) Other Functions	Sector of expenditure				
			Component Bodies and Research Units	Grant-aided Associations	University Grants	University Training	Total
D3. Conservation—Nature Reserves and sites of special scientific interest	B8; D1-2, 4	(i) S.S.R.C. (ii) H.O., F.C.O., D.O.E., M.o.D., L.A.s	1,064	—	9	54	1,127
D4. Pollution of land and wildlife	C5; D1-3; E4	(i) A.R.C., M.A.F.F. (ii) D.O.E., F.C.O., L.A.s	90	—	22	6	118
D. TOTAL			2,161	35	241	123	2,560
E. Atmosphere E1. Atmospheric physics	B3; C1-2	(i) S.R.C., M.o.D, D.O.E., D.T.I., C.E.G.B., (ii) M.o.D, D.O.E, W.R.B., F.C.	519	—	34	28	581
E2. Ionospherics ...	A8	(i) S.R.C., M.o.D. (ii) M.o.D, P.O., M.A.S.	122	—	—	6	128
E3. Climate	C1-2	(i) M.o.D. (ii) D.O.E., M.o.D., M.A.S.	69	—	11	4	84
E4. Atmospheric pollution ...	A9; D4	(i) S.R.C., M.R.C., A.R.C., S.S.R.C., M.o.D., D.T.I., D.H.S.S., U.K.A.E.A., F.C. (ii) D.O.E., D.T.I., M.o.D., F.C.	—	—	9	—	9
E. TOTAL...			710	—	54	38	802
A–E TOTAL (gross)			10,562	1,201	1,314	667	13,744
A–E Receipts			402	—	—	—	402
A–E TOTAL (net)			10,160	1,201	1,314	667	13,342
H.Q. and central services ...							577
TOTAL net expenditure ...							13,919

TABLE 4

S.R.C. PROGRAMME ANALYSIS
(1970–71 Estimates)

£'000

| Fields of Support | Major Government Agencies etc. Supported | Sector of Expenditure | | University Awards | | | Total |
		Research Establishments and Central University Support Facilities	Research Grants	Fellowships	Studentships	International Contributions	
1. Astronomy	MoD.	2,422	655	1	93	—	3,171
2. Space research	MoD. (Met. Office)	3,204	625	1	34	5,050	8,914
3. Radio research	M.A.S., D.T.I., MoD., P.O., B.B.C., I.T.A.	1,050	30	6	10	—	1,096
4. Nuclear Physics Research	U.K.A.E.A., D.T.I.	11,585	1,520	17	171	6,758	20,051
5. Biological Sciences	D.T.I., A.R.C., M.R.C., N.E.R.C.	—	1,020	103	802	—	1,925
6. Chemistry	D.T.I.	140	970	122	1,324	—	2,556
7. Enzyme Chemistry and Technology	D.T.I., M.R.C.	—	140	—	15	—	155
8. Mathematics	D.T.I., U.K.A.E.A.	—	100	19	631	—	750
9. Neutron Beams	D.T.I.	554	10	—	—	—	564
10. Physics	D.T.I., M.A.S., D.O.E.	28	770	75	583	—	1,456
11. Aeronautical and Civil Engineering	D.O.E.	—	480	3	384	—	867
12. Chemical Engineering	D.T.I.	—	440	3	275	—	718
13. Computing Science	D.T.I.	1,243	540	1	178	—	1,962
14. Control Engineering	D.T.I., P.O., C.E.G.B.	—	440	—	56	—	496
15. Electrical and Systems Engineering	D.T.I.	—	330	—	432	—	762
16. Mechanical and Production Engineering	D.T.I.	—	850	3	318	—	1,171
17. Metallurgy and Materials	D.T.I.	50	1,030	6	297	—	1,383
18. Polymer Science	D.T.I.	10	50	—	29	—	89
19. Transport	D.T.I., D.O.E.	—	—	—	—	—	—
20. London Office Administration		1,126	—	—	—	—	1,126
21. Nato		—	—	—	—	400	400
TOTAL		21,412	10,000	360	5,632	12,208	49,612

APPENDIX D

NOTE ON THE SUPPORT OF RESEARCH
AND DEVELOPMENT IN THE UNITED KINGDOM

1. Government support for R and D (civil and defence together) carried out in the U.K. in 1967–68 totalled approximately £493m. The table opposite sets this figure in the context of all-sector support (totalling £962m. in 1967–68) and shows the various sectors carrying out the work financed by government and others.

TABLE 1

RESEARCH AND DEVELOPMENT CARRIED OUT IN EACH SECTOR ACCORDING TO SOURCE OF FINANCE—EXPENDITURE IN THE U.K. ONLY

1967–68

£'000

Sector providing the funds	Sector carrying out the work						Total amount financed by each sector
	Government	Universities and further education establishments*	Public corporations	Research associations	Private industry	Other	
Government†	217,265	61,517‡	433	4,486	196,012	13,391	493,104‡
Universities	—	5,700	—	—	—	—	5,700
Public corporations	§	400	39,212	1,046	3,559	266	44,483
Research associations	§	—	—	286	370	57	713
Private industry	8,862	3,000	1,443	5,970	335,708‖	5,048	360,031
Overseas	5,423	1,400	534	1,172	21,585	160	30,274
Other	7,124	3,147	10	—	12,603	4,878	27,762
Total cost of research and development carried out in each sector	238,674	75,164	41,632	12,960	569,837	23,800	962,067

Source: Department of Education and Science

* Academic year 1966–67.
† The figures in this line are based on returns from the sectors carrying out the work.
‡ Including £1,849,000 financed by local government.
§ Included in private industry.
‖ Research and development budgets. Other monies earned (about £12·6 million) by R. & D. departments of private industry and used for their R. & D. programmes are included under ' Other'.

TABLE 2
RESEARCH AND DEVELOPMENT IN THE U.K. 1961-1971

Sector Providing Funds	1961–62 £m	as a % of (4)	1964–65 £m	as a % of (4)	1967–68 £m	as a % of (4)	(1970–71) (Estimates)¶ £m	as a % of (4)
Government Support								
1. Total Civil...	139·3‡	36·2	171·9‡	40·3	259·4‡§	53·5	350·0	60·3
2. 'Research Council' element* in (1) ...	24·0†	6·2	38·0†	8·9	57·1‡	11·8	93·8	16·2
3. Total Defence	245·7‡	63·8	255·1‡	59·7	225·9‡	46·5	230·0	39·7
4. Total Civil and Defence (as Returned by Government) i.e., (1)+(3)	385·0‡	100·0	427·0‡	100·0	485·3‡	100·0	580·0	100·0
	£m	as a % of (10)	£m	as a % of (10)	£m	as a % of (10)	£m	as a % of (10)
5. Total Civil and Defence as Returned by Sectors Carrying Out the Work ...	378·2‡	57·5	421·2‡	54·6	493·1‡	51·3	n/a	—
6. Universities (own funds) ...	1·3‡	0·2	1·8‡	0·2	5·7‡	0·6	n/a	—
7. Private Industry and Public Corporations (including R.A.s)	266·2‡	40·5	311·6‡	40·4	405·2‡	42·1	n/a	—
8. Funds from Overseas	12·0‡	1·8	20·8‡	2·7	30·3‡	3·1	n/a	—
9. Other			16·0‡	2·1	27·8‡	2·9	n/a	—
10. TOTAL	657·7‡	100·0	771·4‡	100·0	962·1‡	100·0	n/a	—

* This heading covers Government support for work now undertaken through the Research Council system. It does *not* include Government support for industrial or more applied work funded by the D.S.I.R. (and subsequently by the Ministry of Technology) and is thus in the years up to and including 1964/65 not comparable with the heading 'Research Councils' used in Table 2 of Statistics of Science and Technology 1970.
† Estimated figures rounded to nearest £m and of lower precision than other figures in Table.
‡ Figures derived from Table 2 of Statistics of Science and Technology 1970.
§ Including £1·8m financed by Local Government.
¶ Figures in this column include expenditure overseas (estimated to total £40m).

2. An analysis of all sector support for R and D carried out in the U.K. since 1961–62 is given above (Table 2). Government support for R and D (civil and defence together) rose from an estimated £385m. in 1961–62 to £485·3m. in 1967–68 with the civil share growing from 36·2 per cent in 1961–62 to 53 per cent in 1967–68. In the same period expenditure on R and D by industry rose from an estimated £266m. in 1961–62 to £405·2m. in 1967–68.

3. Government expenditure overseas on research and development since 1966–67 is given in Table 3 below.

TABLE 3

GOVERNMENT EXPENDITURE OVERSEAS ON R AND D

£ thousand

	1966–67	1967–68	1968–69
Defence	15,930	15,502	19,385
Civil:			
External relations	1,317	1,475	1,402
Roads and transport	3	1	—
Atomic Energy	1,402	973	1,901
Aerospace	3,386	5,426	3,375
M.R.C.	54	58	63
N.E.R.C.	—	2	2
S.R.C.	7,768	9,838	11,612
Other science grants	10	22	37
Agriculture, fisheries and forestry	5	5	6
Health and welfare	—	—	—
TOTAL civil	13,945	17,800	18,399
TOTAL civil and defence	29,875	33,302	37,784

Note: Figures for 1966–67 and 1967–68 are derived from Table 15 in Statistics of Science and Technology 1970, and those for 1968–69 from Economic Trends November 1970.

Produced in England for Her Majesty's Stationery Office by Commercial Colour Press London

Dd.251711 K8 3/73